25 Home Practices and Tools [partially covered by label] ess

THE ULTIMATE GUIDE TO SELF-HEALING

VOLUME 4

LAURA DIFRANCO

Featuring: Esther Apoussidis, Shannon Berk, Laura Buckley, Lynda Carpenter, Kimberly Fisher, Susan Gaertner, Amy Gillespie, Anne-Marie Harnett, Stacey Herrera, James Kawainui, Veronica B. Light, Shellie Mekash, Linda Aileen Miller, Mandy Morris, Kelly Myerson, Cedric Nwafor, Jen Piceno, Dr. Elle Provencher, Ektaa Rajani, Dinahsta "Miss Kiane" Thomas, Dorothy Tome, Meredith Vaish, Hemali V. Vora, Karin M. Yearwood

The Ultimate Guide to Self-Healing Volume 4
25 Home Practices and Tools for Peak Holistic Health and Wellness
Laura Di Franco, MPT

Blue Whispers of Truth

by Jo Jayson

Blue governs the Throat or 5th chakra, representing knowledge, independence, and communication. It is the center of self-expression and self-honesty. 'Blue Whispers of Truth' is the expression of the 'essence' of the color BLUE in particular its association with this chakra. It speaks of the truth of ourselves, the expression of our creativity and our beliefs. It is expansive and limitless like the sky. 'Blue Whispers of Truth' connects us to our own personal truth and enables us to find the courage to communicate compassionately, yet standing strong in our own convictions. Blue is the energy of peace, expansion and communication. www.JoJayson.com

DEDICATION

To the men and women who stepped up to help me heal the world; thank you. The authors of these books are true healers. They understand the journey. They understand that empowering their clients to heal themselves is the biggest gift they give. They walk the path with awareness, authenticity, courage and an indomitable spirit. I'm incredibly honored to be here among them, guiding this book project. I've pinched myself every day since it began. And this time, when that boring voice said, who am I to do this? I had a different answer than in the past. Laura Di Franco is my name, and Brave Healing is my game. I'm here to change the world with my words! This book is dedicated to every soul who helped me stand up and say that out loud with fire in my voice. I'm now helping others find their fire, and share their powerful words and voices with the world. Thank you. The ripple is real.

INTRODUCTION

I woke up on March 20, 2020 from a dream. After days of pure panic about my entire physical therapy business being shut down in a single day during the pandemic, I'd been practicing everything I preach. *You don't know the bigger picture yet,* I thought to myself. And with a deep, full breath, *what else is possible here?*

Dwelling in that one question has served me more ways than I can count. So that morning, I remembered to follow the feeling of possibility. I slipped out of bed, pulled my sweats on and walked into the kitchen. *You've been wanting to do this for like four years,* I heard the voice say, *why now? Because the world needs us right now,* I replied, lifting up the silver top of my MacBook and hurrying to a Facebook group where my lovely healer goddesses hang with me.

"Ladies, who wants to write a chapter with me?" I typed, "The world needs to know how to heal at home right now and we can teach them."

In 48 hours I had all 24 yeses. Five weeks later, The Ultimate Guide to Self-Healing was born with powerful stories and simple tools that the reader could do at home. From that morning until the very moment I type these words in volume 4, something much bigger than me has been driving this bus. All I've been doing is following orders. Being in the abundant flow in such a powerful way has solidified my knowing that when you align with joy you're an unstoppable force of good. This book is part of that energy.

In fact, what you'll read here is all pure, powerful, palpable energy from 25 expert authors. They step up into their authentic selves in their stories for you, and then they drop their expertise in the form of teaching a tool you can practice as you read. Take a moment with that same deep, full breath I took and ask yourself:

What else is possible for my healing today?

Dwell in the question. Because you might just be about to learn something that could change everything.

Another question to answer here, right up front, is why holistic healing? I mean, isn't any kind of healing great? Ask any experienced healer and they will tell you that authentic healing must be holistic. That means the incorporation and integration of mind, body, soul and spirit. Because all our wounds affect all of who we are. A physical injury always has mental, emotional and spiritual components. A mental or emotional insult always has physical components. Every single emotion you feel has a physiology in your body. To only address one aspect of you would be to miss a big part of the picture. Addressing only one part of the picture usually ends up in temporary or partial results in terms of healing.

When I put the call out to my healer friends that morning I already knew who I was asking to assist me. Aside from being badasses, these holistic healers roll with integration in mind. They know if they address your back pain, but forget to ask you about the job or loved one you lost this month, they'll miss a big opportunity to help you heal. They know if they address your back pain, but forget to tie in your entire body system into their evaluation, they'll miss another opportunity for more complete healing. And most of all they know that if they don't empower you to connect to your own inner guide, healer, and wisdom, they'll never be doing what they should to help you with the most powerful way to heal that there is; YOU!

You'll enjoy a very holistic approach on these pages and you may notice repeating themes such as a connection to the breath, enhancing your intuition, or becoming aware of what you're thinking. There are some basic, foundational principles of healing that are so key it bears repeating them. The most important thing to catch yourself saying? "I already know that." Drop into a beginner's mind, the true mark of a master, and dwell in the possibility that there might be something new about that particular topic that you haven't heard before.

Enjoy the journey!

SPECIAL NOTE TO THE READER

There's something in the healing world that we call the Healing Crisis. It's a form of awareness I'd like you to know about as you dive in to these pages. A healing crisis happens when we're feeling the energy of an old injury, pain or past trauma as it's coming up to be released or healed. That resistance comes up in you in the form of thoughts, sensations, feelings, emotions, and sometimes memories that don't feel good. Notice your habitual reactions to them. Sometimes it's exactly what you're having the most resistance around (words, ideas, practices, conversations, etc..) that are the biggest opportunity for healing. Skilled healers recognize this, and assist their clients through it with tools such as dialoguing, energy work, hands-on practices and modalities, and mindset and awareness coaching.

The healing crisis and your own resistance are each an opportunity to go a layer deeper. They are doors to release and relief. And sometimes, it feels so bad you think you'll die. Please know that we (author-healer-experts) get it. And we're here for you.

If you purchased this book, you'll enjoy access to a very special Facebook group called The Ultimate Guide to Self-Healing Community, where our author experts are hanging out to help answer your questions and provide you with live training. This is an incredible benefit. Make sure to take advantage of it, especially if you're stuck or have questions about what you're feeling. You're not alone. We're here to help you. Your questions will be welcomed and your concerns will be honored. You'll have a safe space to do this work of healing.

See you there!

DISCLAIMER:

This book offers health and nutritional information and is designed for educational purposes only. You should not rely on this information as a substitute for, nor does it replace professional medical advice, diagnosis, or treatment. If you have any concerns or questions about your health, you should always consult with a physician or other healthcare professional. Do not disregard, avoid, or delay obtaining medical or health-related advice from your healthcare professional because of something you may have read here. The use of any information provided in this book is solely at your own risk.

Developments in medical research may impact the health, fitness, and nutritional advice that appears here. No assurances can be given that the information contained in this book will always include the most relevant findings or developments with respect to the particular material.

Having said all that, know that the experts here have shared their tools, practices, and knowledge with you with a sincere and generous intent to assist you on your health and wellness journey. Please contact them with any questions you may have about the techniques or information they provided. They will be happy to assist you further!

CONTENTS

CHAPTER 1

AWARENESS

THE FOUNDATION FOR AUTHENTIC HEALING

BY LAURA DI FRANCO, MPT

MY STORY

"Awareness is everything." I fidgeted in the driver's seat and turned to face my sister as I said these words. "But what do you mean by self-sovereignty?" Something she said gave me that all-too-familiar pause; the sensation inside me I'd grown to trust is my deepest knowing, my intuition, and the voice to pay attention to.

"My yoga teacher said it's when you realize that you have what you need inside, that your unique creative expression is the goal. She said you could learn the dance, but that the real dance is the one you create from those moves, but in only the way you can do it. You have to make it yours."

We were talking about our training and mastery of our fields of study. "I don't think I need to take one more course," I said with a puff of my lips.

Then my brow wrinkled, and I exhaled hard.

"What if my dance is jumping up and down for three hours at a rave with my hands in the air screaming at the top of my lungs? Don't you think I might mow people over with that dance? Am I supposed to suppress it?"

I always thought of myself as an alien with a weirdly extraordinary amount of energy. The divorce was the catalyst for my alien transformation, but the steady commitment to joy that followed was what sealed the deal for me. And raving.

I have the secret to everything. And awareness is the key. Suppose I stay aware of what's happening in my moments in terms of joy. In that case, I have absolutely everything I need to do and be everything I want, including things like rich, energized, motivated, healthy, athletic, funny, creative, and a badass at my business.

"No, you don't need to suppress it. What if that's the exact energy other people need to feel?" She challenged my doubt.

"Can you believe that 2020 is the year we got to visit with each other in person twice? I've seen you more this year than the last five combined. What is wrong with us?" I laughed, and my sister nodded in agreement, laughing hard enough that a little spit came out of her mouth and onto the floor of the passenger seat of the Mustang.

OMG, she's spitting COVID into my car, I thought. But why I cared at that point is a little beyond me, even as I write this. We'd already hugged. We'd already spent more than fifteen minutes less than six feet from each other. Hey Mom, it is what it is. Just relax.

"Everyone is so stupid," she said. "Oh, you mean, including us?" I replied. We both laughed. And then it was silent. You know that moment when you're talking to someone, and you both realize something at the same time, and there's nothing much to say about it because it's a little too late to change your mind?

See, to practice a lack of stupidity about COVID or any other important thing, you'd have to be practicing awareness and making good decisions before you take action. You know, like hugging your sister who's been cavorting in a house full of people you don't know, after riding a plane from California to D.C.

Yeah.

It's okay; you can call me stupid if you want. I get it. And by the way, I'm healthy. And so are my family. After almost a year of this trauma, we are doing pretty good. I haven't been the only one to break the rules. But we've been using our masks and washing our hands, and respecting the quarantine suggestions if any of us were knowingly exposed.

"I should get back," my sis said, "I told them eleven, and it's eleven-thirty."

"I don't want you to go," I said, "I love you, and I hope you have a safe flight back. I popped the trunk. Remember to grab your bag." "Okay," she said. "I love you too."

I had like three more hours' worth of stuff I wanted to talk about, but we'd already been talking for that long. Chats with my sister over the years since we both became healers are always magnificent; full of a ninja-level of awareness, each of us saying the exact thing the other needs to hear to spur an idea, the perspective, the Aha, and the forward growth and evolution. My sister and I have traveled a bizarre parallel healing journey, even though we've lived on opposite coasts for those journeys for over three decades. We share a love of the process, a passion for deeper awareness, and lifelong seeking as our calling. To have someone like that in my life has been the greatest blessing.

Self-sovereignty, I thought as I watched her disappear in my side mirror. *What is my dance*, I wondered. She waved. Her face was sad. So was my heart. I reached my palm to the center of my chest and rubbed a bit. *I'll journal when I get home*, I thought, *I think this is it, I need to dance my dance from now on until I die.*

I could feel the ache in my chest. I feel like it's what must happen to twins when they're separated. My sis and I have that kind of connection. I think we always have. I remember telling her on the phone one day, "God, I was up all night. It felt like I drank an espresso." "Me too!" She said. "Oh, I wonder if that's why. Maybe I was feeling your stuff."

Hang with healers long enough, and that's what your conversations will sound like. Magical juju most people would hear and think, WTF? But it's conversation I've grown to crave more of. Being able to share magical-feeling moments with someone who not only gets it but practices the same magic is a gift. It's part of why this book you're reading was born; to give you that gift. I want you to ask yourself every single day, "What's possible?"

My practice of awareness is a combination of body awareness, thought awareness, self-reflection, journaling, and sacred conversation with others who practice. It has a foundation of three decades of training in holistic healing and physical therapy and fourteen years of training in the marital art of Tae Kwon Do. It includes the practice of modalities like breathwork, John F Barnes Myofascial Release, emotional freedom technique, CranioSacral therapy, Reiki, acupuncture, meditation and mindfulness, and so many more that I'd end up typing to the end of the chapter with that list. In short, my whole life has been about awareness, the different forms of it, and the different ways to use it to pursue joy and peak health and happiness. I would say my black belt is in awareness.

I've used awareness to survive a journey through unworthiness, heal childhood wounds, and deal with disappointments, death, and divorce. And not just deal with those things, but thrive through them. I've relied on my awareness to give me the answers to the biggest possible questions, make huge-ass decisions, and guide others when their pain was too great to bear. I've practiced awareness in a way that's helped me attract abundance; energy, money, time, experiences, joy, etc. And most recently, I've used it to navigate a serious family event that has threatened to consume us with negativity, fear, and doubt.

The gift of awareness comes in moments you remember to practice, moments you practice a little sooner than the last time, and moments you realize you've mastered a moment and have already taken action through the fear. These are moves, just like in my martial arts practice, that become automatic, ingrained in body and mind, and ready when needed.

Got awareness?

Let's practice some ninja awareness moves now!

THE TOOL

The cool thing about awareness (the practice of body and thought observation) is you can do it anywhere, no matter what you're doing. Right, no excuses.

While formal meditation practices are amazing, I'm not asking you to sit on a pillow for an hour with your legs crossed. I'm asking you to notice what you feel and think. I know you can do this. It's a matter of being able to do it when you're struggling, challenged, or otherwise fearful or doubting. It's a matter of being able to do it when you're in pain, physical, mental, or emotional. And that move, my friends, is the move of a warrior. Why? Because you were taught not to feel. You were taught to think and feel how others thought was right. You have to be a warrior to unlearn and re-train yourself.

So while this tool is very simple, do not be fooled. It will take daily practice, and just when you think you've mastered it, life will most likely give you a chance to up-level; a challenge will be presented that throws you back into your ruminating mind. I call this the pit. I get dumped into the pit of fear, worry, and doubt all the time. It's just that I now know how to get back out. In fact, I'm getting really good at not falling in as much at all. This is what I want for you. It's going to take some dedication and perseverance. And it's going to be the most magical, badass, amazing thing you've ever done for yourself.

With awareness, you get a choice. When you practice awareness, you get to choose things like love, joy, peace, freedom, gratitude, and positivity. Assuming these things sound good to you, let's do this. What you do, you are. So getting into action with this practice is the most important thing you can do today. To listen to an audio recording of the body awareness exercise below, you can visit: https://lauradifranco.com/brave-book-resources/

Here's a three-step process of awareness. Step one is the pre-awareness homework. Steps two and three are the actual practice.

WHAT DO YOU WANT?

Step one is about what you want. Grab a journal and pen and take a few breaths. Write down anything that comes to you regarding the feelings and things you want for your life. Don't censor this. Imagine a limitless supply of resources and no restrictions. How do you want to feel? What do you desire? What do you want? Write it all out. Give yourself plenty of time to do this.

Often, we get to a point in our lives when we've checked off everything on the to-do list of what was supposed to make us happy, only to find that we aren't. Often, the problem is that everything on that list was what someone else told you should make you happy, not what actually makes you happy. So for this journaling, focus on the feelings, things, and moments that bring you a feeling of joy.

When I first did this exercise, I sat for a long time and thought, *I have no fucking clue what I really want.* And that is fine. I suggest giving yourself more time to ponder the question. And I suggest starting with anything that makes you feel good. Your list and descriptions will evolve from there. And those things will change! It's okay that they change. Honor what you're feeling at this moment, and write from that place. That's why it's about the journey, every moment of it, and not getting to a perfect destination.

Next, we start to really feel and master the practice of noticing what we're feeling and thinking.

WHAT DO YOU FEEL?

Step 2 is to notice what you're feeling and thinking. This is the main, most powerful practice of awareness. Noticing what you're feeling, sensing, thinking, and how you're reacting could just be the answer to most problems you have. It's that powerful. When you master the practice of noticing, you then get a choice about how you want to proceed. If you have a negative thought, you get the choice to clear your mind. If your body is tightening in response to a stressor, you get a choice to relax those muscles. If you're about to go off on someone who just angered you with something they said, with awareness, you get a choice to respond calmly, in a way that dissolves the hurt and possibly resolves a conflict. If you're trying to make a big decision about your career or a relationship, with awareness, you'll have a direct connection to a higher source through your intuition, and you will receive clear messages about what to do next.

Awareness is everything!

If you'd like to listen to an audio of this body awareness exercise, you can do that here: https://lauradifranco.com/brave-book-resources/

You can practice awareness in moments you dedicate to just that, or you can practice in any moment you wish, even if you're doing something else. The first option listed is for when you can really relax and close your eyes. The second option is a version you can do any time, anywhere.

VERSION 1

Find a comfortable position, close your eyes, and begin to relax. Take deeper breaths, one after another, allowing your whole body to relax on the exhales. Allow the weight of your body to sink into the chair or surface you're on a little more each time you exhale. Relax through your head, neck, throat, and jaw. Soften and melt. Relax through your shoulders, allowing them to drop down away from your ears. Relax your chest and upper back, releasing and softening your body with each exhale. Breathe deeply into your belly, allowing your ribs to expand out all sides with the inhale. Release the weight of your body on the exhales, a little more with each breath.

Begin to bring your awareness to your body and to your thoughts. What do you notice? Can you feel the weight of your body on the chair? The clothes on your body? The temperature in the room? Do you hear any sounds? What do you taste or smell? What thoughts are in your mind? Do you have worries showing themselves repeatedly? Is your to-do list running through your mind? Do you notice judgments about others or circumstances? Begin to clear your mind and drop your awareness to the body and to the sensations of the breath, allowing those sensations to be what you focus on.

Optional Journaling: Set a timer for 5 minutes and fill in the blank: I feel ______. Try not to censor the writing. Write as fast as you can, whatever thoughts or feelings are moving through you.

VERSION 2

You can do everything in version one no matter where you are. All it takes is a change of focus and noticing what's going on. Try bringing awareness to your body, noticing the muscle tension, and relaxing with the breath. Notice the thoughts in your mind and how they're making you react. Pause. Breathe. What would be a better, healthier way to think, believe, or respond right now?

And that gets me to the choice you have now. When you're aware, you can flip your switch from negative to positive, or from negative to neutral, in any given moment. Let's take this one step further and talk about how to do that. This is for warrior ninjas, y'all.

CHOOSE SOMETHING BETTER

Step three is flipping your switch. Esther Hicks calls it the pivot. When you're aware of muscle tension in the body, you have a choice to unclench and soften. When you're aware of negative, self-sabotaging, or judgmental, toxic thoughts, you have a choice to clear your mind. And when you're noticing all of the sensations, feelings, thoughts, and reactions you're having, you get the choice to either flip to neutral (stop thinking and just breathe) or flip to joy (choose to think, believe, and feel happy, grateful, or totally blissed out). I realize that totally blissed out is tough, depending on what challenge your moment is bringing you. However, just flipping to "neutral," a space of relaxation with the breath, without thought or judgment, is going to help shift your energy, raise your vibration, and move you in a better direction.

We can't always flip from the crap to the joy. We need a bridge sometimes. So a deep, relaxing, clear-minded breath can be the ticket. Just stopping making the feeling mean anything can be a game-changer.

Now, for you ninjas who want to take this to a whole other level of badass manifesting skills, what about flipping to what aligns with your deepest desires? Remember step one? Yeah, that juicy goodness. How about you notice, take the breath, and then choose whatever makes you feel the best? Whatever inspires you? Whatever thought, belief, mantra, affirmation, or action will be the change you want to make in your life. When you're in that moment, you're living that better moment. You're not only creating who you want to be, you are who you want to be. And isn't it cool that with awareness, you get to do that in any moment you choose? Damn right it's cool!

Carry on, warriors! And use this practice as you read through the rest of this amazing book and the tools you're being offered here. Use awareness to pick up on what you're feeling and thinking as you read. Notice. Don't judge it. Just notice. Every moment is an opportunity for healing.

Laura Di Franco, MPT spent 30 years in holistic physical therapy and 12 of those in private practice before making a pivot with her company, Brave Healer Productions. With 14-years of training in the martial arts and 19 books, including 11 Amazon best sellers, she's got a preference for badass in every way.

Laura brings her master-level training and knowledge to the table as a certified content marketer with SmartBlogger, a writing-coaching student with NYT Best Selling author Laura Munson, business and speaking coaching student with the Quantum Leap coaching program, Marie Forleo's B-School and The Copy Cure, Jeff Walker's Product Launch Formula, Jack Canfield's author training, and Odette Peek's public speaking training, among others.

Her daily calling is to help you do what you need to do to change the world in less time and with fewer mistakes and heartache on the journey. She shares her authentic journey, wisdom, and expertise with refreshing transparency and straight forward badassery. Hold on to your seat because riding alongside her means you'll be pushed into and beyond your comfort zone and having way more fun with your purpose-driven fears on a regular basis.

When Laura chills out, you'll find her with a mojito at a poetry event with friends, driving her Mustang, bouncing to the beat at a rave, or on a beach in Mexico with something made of dark chocolate in her mouth. Joy is the way she healed herself. Ask her about that sometime. www.BraveHealer.com

CHAPTER 2

OH ____! I HAVE CANCER, NOW WHAT?

THE MINDSET YOU NEED

LYNDA CARPENTER, MS CAM

MY STORY

Can you imagine shaking hands with the grim reaper and walking away, better for the introduction? I had stage four, metastatic, supposedly terminal cancer. It started in the breast, went to the bone in three places, and when it got to the intestine, my oncologist signed papers saying I was terminal—the death benefit on my life insurance policy paid in 2011. I loved spending that money! Then, after focus and dedication to my overall health and wellness, in 2016, my PET/CT read, "No foci of hypermetabolic activity are identified." I believe I was clear long before that, but I went three years without a PET/CT. Somewhere in there, I reversed the cancer. I did it all holistically. I never received conventional chemotherapy or radiation. When my oncologist got the results, he said one word, "Amazing!" This chapter will discuss the *most* important component of healing from cancer.

THE TOOL

Mindset – only you are in control.

Little is more frightening than surgery, chemotherapy and radiation. Then there is "Oh wait, what if I don't make it? Oh no, my husband (or wife)...my children, my family, my pet, my career...? Yep, that is where it starts:

Oh _____! I have cancer! Now what?

However, you need to understand something.

No matter the disease name, no matter the stage of the disease, no matter the prognosis stated by anyone, there have been people, clear on their commitment to health, who have overcome the disease, even on the brink of death. You, too, can regain your health.

Above all, your mindset is the *most* important component in regaining your health. Your beliefs do create your reality. Henry Ford said, "If you think you can or you think you can't, you're right." Bruce Lipton has validated scientifically that genetic expression is based on perception. You can read about it in his remarkable book, *The Biology of Belief* (Hay House, 2008).

It will serve you to understand that I am not particularly "woo woo," and I am not particularly religious. I have to have the science. The interesting fact is that science validates both religion and energy medicine (what is often seen as "woo woo").

Imagine, for a moment, a large field. This field has not been plowed or mowed or kept in any way. It's not a meadow with green grasses or a forest knoll. It's a barren field—something of a wasteland. But there is growth. What grows in a field like this? Well, nothing unless there is water and some seeds. Then, mostly weeds. There are tall weeds and short weeds and weeds of various colors. But when it's all said and done, it's a chaotic field of weeds. Now, picture a beautiful vegetable garden with straight rows and vegetables ready to produce. There is broccoli, cauliflower, kale, tomatoes, peppers, and squash (the latter three are botanically a fruit but most think of them as vegetables). There are rows and mounds, and everything grows where it is intended, and production is beautiful and life-giving.

What is the difference between the two fields? Instructions. Yes, Instructions. The vegetable garden was given instructions on what to grow and where to grow it. And any gardener knows that there are specific rules to follow for success; rules like not planting tomatoes in the winter and plant in the sun, not shade. Now you *could* spread random seeds and water, and some plants might actually produce something, but it won't produce the optimum garden.

Your DNA is like the seeds that you would plant in a garden. When seeds are given proper soil, sunlight, and water, they produce healthy vegetables and fruits. When your DNA is given instructions from you—your mindset which produces your thoughts—along with the dietary nutrients and a non-toxic environment, they produce a rather amazing harvest of healthy cells. Dr. Joe Dispenza says, "Your DNA is a parts list of potentials waiting for instructions from you." He also says, "If you want a new outcome, you will have to break the habit of being yourself, and reinvent a new self." He wrote a great book called *Breaking the Habit of Being Yourself: How to Lose Your Mind and Create a New One.* (Hay House, 2012)

Reinventing a new self is mindset. What are some of the habits that keep you you?

- Sleep on a particular side of the bed
- Get up at ____ o'clock
- Pee
- Brush your teeth
- Make coffee/tea
- Check Facebook (or whatever social media, text, email, or chat)
- Shower

Those habits might not be so detrimental, but what about:

- The sugar in that pot of coffee/tea
- Going to bed at midnight (not getting a good night of healing sleep)
- Having sugar-based cereal for breakfast or bacon with nitrates and other toxins
- Eating toxin-rich processed, fast, and junk food

- A high-stress job that produces anxious feelings or anger or feelings of inadequacy
- Staying in an unsupportive relationship
- Lack of exercise

Those are some habits that keep you, you. What other habits keep you, you?

Consider what habits would the healthy you have?

- Wake up after eight hours of restful sleep
- Drink some water (at least eight ounces) to rehydrate you. Maybe add a drop of lemon essential oil to support cleansing, good salt for the minerals and electrolytes, and cayenne pepper for the capsicum.
- Do some yoga, Qi Gong, or other nourishing exercises
- Have a vegetable smoothie or green juice daily
- Eat a healthy, organic, plant-strong diet with clean, organic meats that ate their natural diet for their whole life (rather than commercially produced beef, chicken, pork, or lamb).
- Manage your stress. Establish self-care.
- Meditate on gratitude daily

This is not rocket science, but it is critical. Every time you employ the habit of a healthy person instead of an unhealthy person, you're giving instructions to your DNA to produce an amazing harvest of healthy cells. Much, if not all, of health can be influenced by your thoughts and the actions produced by them. Start shifting your mindset into a person of overall health and just watch and see what can happen in your body.

Speaking of thoughts, even people who are not particularly religious tend to say a few prayers after hearing their name and cancer in the same sentence. That prayer may go out with different intensities, but it is still prayer.

In her book, *Radical Remission: Surviving Cancer Against All Odds* (Harper One, 2015), Dr. Kelly Turner states that "Deepening one's spiritual connection (whatever you call it) is one of the ten key factors in surviving and even reversing cancer."

Let's talk about how to make it most effective. Yes, there are ways to make sure your prayer, meditation, introspection, self-reflection, or quiet time are "heard" and are most effective.

First, there are four well-known modes of prayer. Colloquial prayer or informal prayer is like saying Grace over dinner. Petitionary prayer is asking for something. It's like asking for someone's healing or a new job or a great parking space. Ritualistic prayer is formal. The Lord's prayer is an example of ritualistic prayer. Then there is meditative prayer (some purists dispute that this is a type of prayer). Meditative prayer is to sit in meditation and consider the awe of the Spirit or God or whatever you praise. Deepak Chopra distinguishes prayer vs. meditation this way: "Prayer is you speaking to God. Meditation is allowing the Spirit to speak to you."

What Gregg Braden discusses as the "lost mode of prayer" was first described in *The Gospel of Thomas. The Gospel of Thomas* was one of the books that was edited out of the bible by Emperor Constantine around 400 years after Jesus's death. The translation instructs, "To ask without hidden motive, be surrounded by your answer and be enveloped by what you desire." What that means (as interpreted by Gregg Braden) is, ask for what you want (not what you don't want) and feel the feeling (be surrounded by your answer). Feel the feeling of getting what you ask for (be enveloped by what you desire).

The way I say it is this: If your prayer has words, you're speaking the wrong language. The language of Spirit, God, the Universe (whatever you call it) is FEELINGS. Feel the feeling of what it feels like to be done with cancer. "Oh, wow, I am healthy! Now what?" Feel it in present tense. How does it feel to be done with cancer and all that it entails? Then add as many of your five senses to that as you can. When you are clear of cancer, what will you see? (Your test results? Smiles on your loved one's faces? A smile looking back at yourself in the mirror? What else?)

What will you hear? What will you say to others? What will you say to yourself? What will they say to you? (Your doctor giving your test results? Maybe your doctor saying, "This is amazing!" Your friends saying, "Congratulations!"). You get the idea. What do you feel physically? Maybe you have more energy; maybe body parts work better, maybe you feel like a weight was lifted. You certainly feel a sense of relief. Are there smells and tastes associated with being totally healthy? You might toast a glass of green juice with someone who supported you. Maybe you take a trip to the ocean or the mountains and enjoy the smells of fresh air and salt or the pine or spruce or fir of the forest. The more senses you add, the stronger the communication to Spirit or whatever that force is that science can now validate.

When I was pursuing health, my feelings included an uncontainable happy dance.

I meditated on this every day. At the time, we were traveling in an RV. We went on what we were afraid might be our last hurrah. I would get up early (I am naturally an early riser) and go outside and do about 45 minutes of yoga to the rising sun. What a spectacular time that was. Immediately following yoga, I would spend 16 minutes in meditation. I used an eight-minute meditation song and would let it play twice. The first eight minutes were just paying attention to my breathing, slowly in and out. I followed my breath from my nose to the back of my throat, down my breathing tube to my lungs, to the little air sacs. I would focus on breathing all the way to my core, in and out slowly and gently. The second eight-minutes was to think of something or someone that I was grateful for on the inhale and feel the feeling of gratitude for that person or thing on the exhale. In my meditation, there was always time spent on the uncontainable happy dance, that beautiful feeling of being done with cancer.

Gratitude is said to be the most healing emotion. It was truly a great way to start the day. Can you imagine what would happen if the whole world started their day with feelings of gratitude? You can read more about the lost mode of prayer in his book, *Secrets of the Lost Mode of Prayer: Hidden Power of Beauty, Blessing, Wisdom, and Hurt* (Gregg Braden, Hay House, 2005).

An important note: You must also align your thoughts with your feelings. If you are thinking like you can conquer the world and "you've got this," but on the inside, you feel like Vincent van Gogh's, *The Scream*, you are NOT aligned. This may take some practice. This may take a lot of practice.

Okay, let's get real. The first time I tried to think of cancer and gratitude at the same time, it was violent. I have something of an oversized bean bag that I use as a meditation pillow. When it's too cold to meditate outside, I meditate in my sunroom on my poof. My poof is about as big as a square coffee table in both height and diameter. Tipped against the wall, it forms a comfy, cozy place to get in touch with me. The poof was given to me by my brother when I was in high school and has always been special and holds a sense of security for me. I have kept it for over 40 years. It's something of a happy place for me.

Having an understanding of the power of gratitude, I knew that having a true sense of gratitude for the experience of cancer would be both powerful and healing. So, I sat in my happy place on my nurturing meditation pillow (my poof) and tried to think of cancer and gratitude. I screamed, I cried, I cursed, I spit, and I beat the crap out of my poof until I couldn't beat it anymore. It took about two months of practice and a lot of soul searching to get to a point where I could be legitimately grateful for the experience of having cancer.

The documentary film, *The Secret* (Prime Time Productions, 2006) posited that "Gratitude will shift you to a higher frequency, and you will attract much better things." So, get to a point where you can think about cancer with a sense of gratitude. Consider what you have as a result of a diagnosis that you would not have had. Here are some examples:

- Because of cancer, I got to travel.
- Maybe you have qualified for social security and enjoy that income.
- Cancer provides an excuse for virtually anything.
- What have you learned because of cancer?
- Have you repaired relationships because of cancer?
- How has cancer made you special?
- What else? What else? What else?

Here is a big example: There was a living benefits rider on the life insurance policy that I got around the time I turned 30 years old. When my oncologist signed papers saying I was terminal, that life insurance policy paid 50% of the total value. I got a really big check. And no, I didn't have to pay taxes, and I don't have to pay it back, and when I do die (At a very old age peacefully in my sleep), whoever survives me will get the other half. We used that money to pay off our doctor bills, credit cards, and debt and then to buy an RV so that we could go on what we thought would be our last hurrah. We called it a Road Trip FOR a Lifetime. This was just one of the things I discovered that I was thankful for regarding cancer.

If you have a life insurance policy and are considered terminal. Ask your insurance broker if there can be a living benefits rider placed on the policy. Mine was there, and I didn't know it. You might ask if this is the case for you also. The living benefits rider can be added even after diagnosis. Submit the necessary paperwork and have a plan for the money. You might go to an alternative medicine facility in Mexico or Germany or one of the facilities here in the U.S. You might buy an RV as we did or a boat. You might simply pay off debt to reduce stress. Check in and see what is most appropriate for you.

Back to mindset and meditation. If you are new to meditation, start simple and go at your own pace. There are lots of books on beginning a meditation practice. Be easy on yourself. Your mind will wander; that's okay. Bring it back with a nice, cleansing breath. I recommend starting with a piece of music that you like. I like Dhanyavad, by Henry Marshall; you can Google it. Use anything that you like as long as it's relaxing and feels safe. On each inhale, think of something you're thankful for. On each exhale, feel the feeling of appreciation for that thing or person or place. Once you get the hang of it, be thankful for the experience of having had cancer and recovering completely. The cancer is in the past tense; it is already gone. You're healthy, whole, and healed. Focus on *that feeling*. What is your uncontainable happy dance?

Thoughts and feelings are frequency. Feelings produce a stronger frequency signal. That is why your thoughts and feelings must be aligned. If not aligned, your feelings will cancel out the vibration of your thoughts. Make sure that you feel the feeling of success, health, and wholeness. Nicola Tesla said, "If you want to find the secrets of the universe, think in terms of energy, frequency, and vibration." And, Dr. Joe Dispenza said, "It's the elevation of frequency that is causing the body to experience a biological upgrade." Healing from cancer can be experienced as a biological upgrade. A healing mindset is to expect the miraculous and live as if it has occurred.

In this chapter, I hope you understand that the mindset you need is one of a clear commitment to your overall health. This mindset must go beyond meditation into life, meaning you must be clear on your thoughts and feel the feelings, and they must translate to your everyday activities in life. To reverse cancer, you must take a whole-health approach and live your life as a healthy person lives. Your mindset may just make you become the healthiest person you know.

Lynda Carpenter's clients want to take back control of their health and have a more natural approach to wellness. They don't just want another pill; they want to fix the problem. Whether it is cancer or another chronic ailment, Lynda's clients want a clear path to living healthy and happy lives. Her clients want someone they can trust and love that she has a Master's Degree in Complementary and Alternative Medicine to back up her recommendations. She is also a Board-certified Drugless Practitioner and a holistic nutritionist who specializes in the therapeutic use of Essential Oils. She is a Certified Raw Food Educator and Advanced Healing Foods Instructor. She uses several therapies and different types of equipment in her practice.

Lynda has presented from Connecticut to California and from Florida to Texas. She has presented in living rooms, on stages, and teaches at her local college. As a speaker and educator, Lynda has written at facilitated multi-day seminars and workshops on mindset, health, and business. Class titles include:

- The Mindset for Navigating Cancer (recording available below)
- Gastro-Esophageal Reflux Disease: A Natural Non-toxic Approach
- Osteoporosis Prevention and Management
- Reversing Autoimmune Disorders
- Cleaning Up Your Cleaners
- Non-toxic Personal Care
- Natures Medicine Cabinet

And many more

Lynda's unique perspective on wellness and healing comes from starting out in conventional medicine, making the switch to alternative approaches to navigate her own cancer successfully. She has an understanding from all three perspectives that healthcare providers and practitioners who haven't walked that path can't possibly appreciate.

When Lynda is not studying, teaching, or writing, you can find her snuggling with her husband, Erick or tending to her greenhouse and garden. She still loves to travel in her RV as well as internationally. You can find more information about Lynda and register for her many online courses or schedule a consultation at www.WellnessFORaLifetime.com.

CHAPTER 3

BALANCING CODEPENDENCE

FINDING SELF-ACCEPTANCE AND PERSONAL POWER

JEN PICENO, SHAMANIC PRIESTESS & ENERGY MEDICINE PRACTITIONER, ORDM, RTM, LMT, THP

MY STORY

Here's the truth: self-acceptance and personal power require you to get honest with yourself. I'm gonna shoot straight with you here. The path to personal power is not for the fainthearted or for those seeking a magic wand for instant gratification.

I don't believe codependence magically goes away. That's coming from a woman who's tried to banish it more than once. It doesn't work that way! You must lean in and flirt with it a bit to understand its odd sense of humor and beautiful complexity. Get comfortable with the idea that it's yours to keep and your responsibility to keep it in check.

Codependence offers an incredible invitation to inner reflection and deep awakening into spiritual maturity. Within the sacred container of spiritual maturity, we see things more clearly.

It took a long time to understand that my people-pleasing addiction was unhealthy and out of control. I positioned myself perfectly in a business of service and prided myself on being the ultimate caretaker, homemaker, and ultimate hero who always saved the day against all odds. The life I created supported my addiction very well. Codependence is quite the trickster!

I thought that women who gave their all, all the time, to everyone but themselves was a selfless way to love and nurture those you care about. When balanced, it's beautiful. But darlin' I was way out of balance. I willingly served others to the point of complete emotional and physical exhaustion, and it was making me ill.

An unfortunate hardship within my marriage took me through some nasty emotional trenches with divine purpose. It gave me a good shake, a kick in the ass, and helped me wake up. We were ready to throw in the towel. Talk therapy didn't work, marriage counseling didn't do the trick, and we were both emotionally drained. Old wounds kept me holding onto a lingering lack of trust, and I overcompensated with people-pleasing, doing, and fixing everything outside of myself. It felt like quicksand dragging me further and further away from what I wanted. I tried my best to forgive the past and move on, but I couldn't forget the heartaches we worked so hard to overcome. Love wasn't the issue. Lots of other things and people got in our way, and we were working ourselves into an early grave. We were pulled in every direction, except the right one. We kept saying "yes" when we wanted and needed to say "no" to everything and everyone. There was zero work-life balance. Exhaustion jolted me and my marriage completely out of alignment and into a bitter state of unhappiness.

I was a master at figuring things out and fixing everything for everyone, but not this time. I was emotionally drained and didn't have the energy to fix anything anymore. I just wanted to run away to a faraway land, but the sacred rebel in me somehow found the strength to keep moving forward.

I had been on my spiritual path for what seemed like forever. I had done so much self-help work, training, and transformational deep dives with amazing healers, teachers, and spiritual leaders. Still, I intuitively knew I needed to go deeper than anything I had previously encountered. I remember feeling led to do more yet completely perplexed at the same time. Seriously, how much healing does a girl gotta do? Well, I'll tell ya from my bright red lips to your ears; it's a lot more than anyone thinks they would ever need to do to get the job done.

Long story short, spirit did what spirit does. I was led to a weekend retreat in the North Carolina mountains. What needed my attention was me. It was a big reveal – an inside job! It was time to take full responsibility and own up to all the places where I betrayed myself. Each time I said "yes" but meant "no" was another self-betrayal. Unconsciously, I was sabotaging my own happiness. My people-pleasing patterns were an external way of seeking approval in all the wrong places. I was trying to make everything better, easier, and more fantastic for everyone except myself. I was avoiding what I needed most, and it wasn't healthy. It was an addiction that kept me from fully loving and accepting myself.

I admit I blamed my husband for one hundred percent of the heartache I carried. There were some big, ugly, thick scars running through the center of my heart with his name, but truth be told, the biggest betrayal was me not honoring myself - which started long before we ever met.

I had unhealed wounds that kept me unbalanced and misaligned. I was doing deep healing work. I was shifting and shedding things layer by layer, and revealing so much in the process. I had some days that were in complete alignment and others that were way out of whack. Like a pendulum, I was swinging from one side to the other, and I was frustrated. My life force energy was depleted, and my physical body was exhausted from not getting it right.

It was so much easier blaming someone else for my unhappiness. This painful but true realization led me to the priestess path. The decision came in while working with a high priestess. I connected deeply with her in sacred ceremony when I stepped into a crystal circle overlooking the mountains. She held my hands as I proclaimed my spirit name, "KatFyre." In ceremony, I balanced my divine feminine and divine masculine energies in sacred marriage of self. I was open and ready for whatever came next and was led to work with her privately.

I felt safe in her sacred space and quickly drifted into a deep shamanic journey while laying on her table with her cats at my feet. I saw scenes from my life play like a movie. She said, "*Go into your heart and look at the flame that resides there.*" What I saw was faint, dim, and weak. She laid her hands on my body, and my heartbeat connected with the heat in her hands.

I drifted deeper into the journey and saw exactly what I needed to see. I was guided by a higher power and, in this connection to spirit, instructed on how to kindle the fire into roaring flames of transformation, much like the best bonfire you've ever seen. She said, "*Where can you let go of next?*" My body surrendered with twitches and shakes. The word TRUST kept appearing. My spirit guides and animals were with me, and my body relaxed as I received a wave of spiritual wisdom. The flames danced with brilliant red and orange. I felt filled with spirit, and heat consumed my body with the most incredible sensations, burning through me with purpose.

My husband and son joined me fireside in this vision. Together we roasted marshmallows on the dancing flames. A clear view of my path was illuminated. I knew my next best step was to commit to the priestess path. The marshmallows were a promise of sweetness for answering the call.

Now, I walk the priestess path and live life in everyday ceremony. The healing journey and each experience played a role in igniting my personal power, keeping the flames dancing, and taught me how to use my energy more wisely.

The wisdom that came through showed me that relationships are mirrors of inner reflection. At times, soulmates tear us wide open and let the light in so we can become the authentic divine being we are called to be. I'm grateful that my husband has held up a mirror for me repeatedly over our twenty years together. Aches and pains, emotional waves, and those annoying cracks that felt like they were breaking my heart wide open have allowed me to balance the unhealthy tendencies of looking outside of myself for approval. It's helped me anchor into the true source of my strength and has taught me to polish the mirror so I can see more clearly.

Soul growth is not pain-free; growing pains are necessary to stretch us into our highest potential. It aligns us with the truth of who we are without negotiation. It supports our spiritual calling with integrity, experience, and inner knowing in a way that cannot be ignored. Yes, it hurts like hell, but it delightfully expands us in ways that nothing else can.

If you are stuck in a place of people-pleasing, not feeling balanced, or are anything less than vibrant, pay attention.

When we sidestep our dreams and desires for any reason, there's always more to the story. This is true for all challenging situations, not just codependent, people-pleasing ones.

When we don't honor ourselves, it's often a sign of suppressed emotions, unhealed spaces, and the wounds of not enough-ness. We get in our own way. That deprives us of happiness. It creates unhealthy busyness that sends us seeking approval outside of ourselves, and we forget to honor and nurture ourselves with fierce love and compassion.

I get it! I understand the need to please. I was willing to do anything for anybody at the expense of happiness, health, and sanity. I allowed people-pleasing to imprison me. It scarred my gypsy soul, destroyed hopes, blocked life force energy, and demolished feminine power.

I was an overachieving multi-talented Queen of Codependence. Yep, I was that girl! Thankfully, there are ways to balance things out and reclaim the essence of who you are so you can regain your sense of power and confidence. I'm living proof!

I had to lean in and accept that people-pleasing is an unhealthy addiction. I constantly agreed to do things I did not want to do, spent time with people I didn't enjoy being around and took on responsibilities that I should have left alone. My stuck-ness was attached to unhealed places blocking my personal power.

There was no balance in that! Thank goodness I found unconventional ways to access inner peace, heal, and connect to my most authentic self. The inner wisdom and soft whispers of my dreams and desires got louder the more I practiced saying no. It wasn't easy at first. In the beginning, it was really uncomfortable. Be forewarned; people don't always support or understand the quest to become a happier, healthier version of yourself. In my case, I pissed off a lot of people. There was resistance, confrontation, and some people were asked to exit my life. I quickly learned who sincerely cared about me and who was around for personal gain at my expense.

Reclaiming my personal power began with the courage to say, "No," and grew stronger when I could say it without guilt or explanation. It has helped me move through experiences with confidence while standing strong in self-acceptance and personal power. It's not always easy, but it's deliciously liberating.

Pairing that with intuition and following inner wisdom has been the key to heal mind, body, and spiritual misalignments. It has balanced me in expansive ways. It has guided my practice and supported me as a healer while taking me down a path of intentional purpose with soulful integrity. My sacred work could not serve others without the fine-tuned skill of hearing, trusting, and following inner wisdom.

Appeasing others while sacrificing my health and happiness has been laid to rest. I've surrendered unnecessary suffering to a higher power and no longer agree to do things I don't want or need to do. I invite you to do the same.

Deciding to do this helped restore my feminine power. Now, I honor my needs and desires, no matter how crazy they seem. This is my recovery secret to balancing things out. I give full credit to the unfulfilling, eye-opening experiences and unsatisfied moments when I said "Yes" to everything and lived life with a fake smile painted on my face. At the time, I didn't recognize my own imbalance of people-pleasing or the dark codependency trap I had willingly placed myself in. Trust the process. When you know better, you do better, and then you feel better.

Learning how to balance things out is never over. It requires paying attention and taking responsibility for ourselves every day. To act in wisdom with self-love, dream big, and honor ourselves with the right to choose what's best for us; it's a lifestyle change. I'm grateful to share my story with you here today so you may make empowered choices and come into balance with intentional purpose.

If you have read this far, most likely you have been overly generous carrying other people's worries, problems, and responsibilities as your own. This is an opportunity to rewrite that outdated story.

The decision is yours. But to be clear, you'll need to turn in your cape and surrender being the hero in every situation. You may have to forfeit the title of being the one everyone counts on to bail them out. As you start your quest toward finding self-acceptance and personal power, you'll gather courage and innate wisdom along the way. You've done lots of hard things in your lifetime, so I know you are strong enough to conquer some uncomfortableness to help you expand and grow. I've found that saying no to what's not right for me is not only the most loving thing I can do for myself, but it often helps others stand up on their own two feet, too.

The more you honor yourself, heal, balance, and align, the more capacity you'll have to love, accept, and attune with the source of your personal power. As we recognize what throws us out of balance, we can self-correct and embody our truths. In the place of truth, we move more easily into our divine birthright of abundance in all forms.

Realigning into divine authenticity is a process of rewriting our story into one we really want. Then, we must love and accept all the bits and pieces within the truth of who we are, including our codependency. My clients have successfully balanced codependency by paying attention to their inner wisdom, nurturing the truth that reveals itself, and trusting what comes through. It creates a safe place for self-acceptance. It's powerful work!

With self-acceptance, we can more easily take intentional steps forward to alchemize the old into a more vibrantly balanced lifestyle. It's a fantastic way to be the hero in your own story, and it makes one hell of an ending.

Don't rush; savor the moment and trust the process. Take time to feel the strength within your blood and bones as you take each soulful step forward. This is to be celebrated. You are making yourself a priority. By doing so, you realign with dreams and desires.

Keep taking steps toward loving and accepting all the layers, bits, and pieces that lay within the truths of codependency. Lean in, then take the next step toward what you want so you can be the hero of your own story.

THE TOOL

ENERGETIC BALANCING

A complimentary audio version is available at:
www.JenPiceno.com/resources

I'm invoking the spirit of fire to ignite personal power and lead us on a magical quest toward change and transformation. Consider lighting a candle to set sacred space, honor the spirit of fire, and your internal flame.

This holds the intention of unblocking dreams and desires while repairing places you may have closed off, betrayed, abandoned, or shut down by putting yourself last on the totem pole. It's designed to empower, create balance, and encourage self-acceptance.

Get cozy as we connect to the highest vibration of light. Feel divine light pouring through the crown of your head and into your body, connecting with the creator of all that is to balance emotional blocks that are limiting your highest potential.

Acknowledge thoughts, feelings, and sensations that arise throughout this process. If something comes up, don't judge it. Just notice it, and send it on its way.

Take full spacious breaths, connecting more deeply with the highest vibration of light while grounding into the earth beneath you. Attune and align with the sacred wisdom being shared from above, below, and within.

Follow your breath into the core of your body, and down into your energetic center, your place of power. Feel the vitality filling you with sacredness. I'm awakening and igniting your personal power. Feel the force of your strength growing bigger, brighter, and more courageous.

Fill yourself completely with transformational light. Allow it to move freely without limitation through your body. The activations are inspiring spiritual awakening, confidence, wisdom, self-love, acceptance, and worthiness. Notice how powerful and alive you feel connected to your divine self. Align with this effortless feeling of peace, power, and balance.

Now, we burn away old agreements blocking your path and remove anything dimming your magnificence so you can enjoy a more vibrant life.

I send the healing spirit of fire to places you feel unappreciated, unloved, or uncertain to unravel and burn unhealthy patterns of unworthiness. Transmuting any places holding fear, grief, anger, sadness, anxiety, or depression now. Ask the spirit of fire to destroy any codependent patterns you wish to surrender. It pops and cracks while burning unwanted attachments and agreements to ash.

Mighty flames are warming your soul and igniting creative sparks of self-acceptance within you. Energetic blocks are transforming into steppingstones, guiding you forward, more empowered, balanced, and free.

Listen as inner wisdom lovingly leads you along your soul's journey. Trust yourself and take the next best step forward.

BONUS: You are invited to receive the channeled light language message that came through while writing this chapter at www.JenPiceno.com/resources

---

Jen Piceno, Priestess, ORDM, RMT, LMT, Shamanic Practitioner is an ordained shamanic priestess and energy medicine practitioner with 30+ years of expertise in the healing arts. Through personalized ceremony, ancestral healing, and channeling light language, she'll help you bust through restrictions so you can solidify your purpose and begin the transformation you've been craving in any area of your life.

Get ready to align with everything you were meant to be in ways you've never experienced before.

Jen is the owner of Gypsy Moon Inc. and a lifetime student of spiritual practices and cultural wisdom found around the world. Jen blends eastern and western modalities with light language, shamanic practices, alchemy, and heart-opening ceremonies. Her work is infused with innovative creativity for soulful experiences that alchemize challenges into purpose.

She is an Ordained Shamanic Priestess in the lineage of StarrFire OrbWeaver, Anyaa McAndrew, and the creatrix, Nicole Christine. Walking the Priestess Path, she celebrates life in everyday ceremony and is committed to making a difference in the lives of others.

Jen offers shamanic healing sessions, personal channeled messages, sacred ceremonies, and private coaching. She is available in person and at her virtual sacred space. Visit: https://www.JenPiceno.com

Stay connected: https://linktr.ee/JenPiceno

CHAPTER 4

EMPOWERED BIRTH IS POSSIBLE

BEING EDUCATED MAKES IT AWESOME!

LINDA AILEEN MILLER, LMT, CD(DONA)

MY STORY

Unwed and pregnant, I left home to give birth and gift my child to strangers.

Normally, when women are anesthetized during birth, they awaken to the sight of their newborn.

In 1969, that was rarely the case for single moms.

After his birth in May, the first face I saw was not my son's. That is what I remember most profoundly from that day.

Much of the rest remains a blur. Snippets pop into my consciousness from time to time. Some of those memories are still painful even now.

I remember judgmental nurses talking about me as if I were deaf, and the lights started going dim.

In the background, I could hear the song, *You'll Never Walk Alone*, playing softly. Our sense of hearing is our last sense to leave. That song has carried me through many days. The poetic, prophetic words etched my first birth in my heart forever.

The face I did see was not my newborn. It was my new best friend who remained by my side for 51 years, for which I am eternally grateful.

My grief was so profound I didn't even name my son for almost thirty years, referring to him only as 'him' in hushed tones to cover my shame.

One thing is clear to me; the circumstances of Michael's birth were instrumental in my choice to become a doula.

I know unequivocally what it feels like to birth with no support.

I want more than that for you!

"I believe no one should ever walk OR birth alone! We have the ability to see and hear with our hearts, stories the body will tell, even without touch if we will only listen."

Linda Aileen Miller, LMT, CD(DONA)

THE TOOL

ADVOCACY, EDUCATION, AND SUPPORT WITH A DOULA

Covid-19 is here, worldwide, and impacting us in ways we never could have imagined. How it has changed birth for you, your partners, your newborn, and the doula world, along with how to work *with* those changes, is my focus.

DONA Certified Birth Doulas are in uncharted territory. Doulas are resiliency at its best. When we come to a fork in the road, we are educated, genius, and skilled at navigating challenges. This will be no different!

Mothers often believe they will have continuous support by their side during labor. Sadly, that was not the case even prior to Covid-19. With overburdened staffs, one can only imagine.

Mom may be on her own to navigate her birth experience with restrictions barring doulas and some fathers or partners from labor and delivery.

Many doulas felt their fear as the pandemic unfolded!

The genius of Penny Simkin, PT, CD(DONA), one of the original founders of Dona International, brought doulas together on March 31, 2020, to shift gears and remind us, "We are all in this together."

I had the privilege of meeting Penny in 2018 at our International Doula Summit. She is a physical therapist who has specialized in childbirth education and labor support since 1968, estimating she has assisted with more than 15,000 births.

During her March 2020 webinar, "Hope" was born anew for doulas, birth moms, partners, and newborns. Once again, Penny 'Doula-ed the Doulas,' holding us as we grieved the loss of the profession we had come to love. She coined the phrase, "Doulas at a Distance," to help us see we still have choices!

I'm choosing to reframe her words ever so slightly here to ***Doulas From a Distance,*** with all due respect.

What is a birth doula? We are advocates, educators, and support persons, primarily for Mom.

As a Certified Birth Doula, my work with families begins three months prior to the due date, offering options that may impact outcomes. Under today's circumstances, this is more valuable than ever!

75% of my work is actually before the first contraction happens.

Education is my job. Helping Mom, Dad, Grandma, and partners know choices in labor can empower them all.

A good advocate supports their choices.

Learning acupressure can be game-changing! We can walk through a lot via a good internet connection!

Did you know a 'double-hip squeeze' encouraging the pelvis to open allows the baby to engage in a more delivery friendly position?

Do you have a Rebozo? I do and will gladly teach you how to use it!

Creating a Birth Box with lots of tools normally packed for delivery day, and teaching you how to use them to calm stress, ease discomfort, and re-start your contractions if they stall, can make a difference.

You have lots of choices!

A BIRTH DOULA SUPPORTS HEALTHY BIRTH OUTCOMES.

Research has proven low infant birth weights, low APGAR scores (Appearance, Pulse, Grimace, Activity, Respiration), the need for epidurals, pitocin, perineal tears, and C-sections, are all negative results which can occur more frequently without continuous labor support from an educated certified doula.

A doula by your side (in person or virtually), from the first contraction until two hours after birth with a latched-on baby on your chest, can help *YOU* make a difference!

In communication with the hospital where the birth is scheduled, I ascertain what their regulations are regarding partners/doulas and more in real-time.

Do they separate moms and newborns if the mother is either infected with Covid or suspected to be?

While this issue is brand new, there have already been studies on it with both the CDC and WHO (World Health Organization) weighing in with totally different approaches. These were the outcomes:

"Data are limited, and recommendations for the first days after birth differ. The World Health Organization (WHO) recommends that infants and mothers with suspected or confirmed COVID-19 should be enabled to remain together and practice skin-to-skin contact, kangaroo care, and to remain together and to practice rooming-in throughout the day and night. Breastfeeding is strongly recommended, given its known lifelong importance for maternal and child health. Mothers are encouraged to wash their hands, wear a mask if they have a cough, and routinely disinfect surfaces that they have touched."

The United States Center for Disease Control and Prevention (CDC) advises that facilities "consider temporarily separating the mother from her infant" until the mother is no longer considered contagious. During the separation, the CDC recommends that women express breast milk to be fed to the newborn by a healthy caregiver. If rooming-in is preferred by the mother or unavoidable due to facility limitations, steps to reduce risk are described. The CDC further suggests " that the risks and benefits of temporary separation should be discussed by the healthcare team', but does not elaborate. (**Reference #1)

The benefit of separation is that it minimizes the risk of transmission of SARS-COV-O2 from mother to infant during the hospital stay. However, if the goal is the health and well-being of mother and child in the months following birth, there are additional considerations.

1. Separation may not prevent infection.
2. Interruption of skin-to-skin care disrupts newborn physiology-17% of infants newborn preemies vs. 92% of newborn preemies in incubators experienced instability.
3. Separation stresses mothers.
4. Separation interferes with the provision of maternal milk to the infant, disrupting innate, and specific immune protection. Breastfeeding is the baby's first vaccine, and skin-to-skin care is important for colonization of the infant microbiome.

(**Reference #2)

This research shows separation doubles the burden on an already burdened hospital staff, requiring more PPE devices for use with the mother and the infant. These factors need to be considered and discussed with your midwife or OB staff before your due date, so we know what the hospital protocol is in the event this becomes a consideration.

With a background in transpersonal psychology, seven years of experience as a CD(DONA) birth doula, and the unwed mother of a son in 1969, I can tell you this:

It absolutely has an impact when mother and baby are separated.

It matters psychologically and physiologically. Breastfeeding outcomes are greatly impacted and thereby impact the immunity established for a newborn in the weeks and months ahead.

At the very minimum, the CDC recommends separated newborns receive milk, which has been 'expressed' or pumped by the biological mother and fed to the newborn by a healthy caregiver. If the birth mom is fortunate enough to have Dad or a partner permitted during labor, they would be the ideal choice to enable early bonding and skin-to-skin bare chest contact holding.

We are definitely in a new world. To that world, we will adapt.

Are doulas capable of producing beneficial results even when they aren't in the room? Statistics show the answer is YES!

Doulas offer support. We educate. We advocate for higher outcomes.

Teaching you how to **ask** for what you want to achieve for the most positive outcomes is vital.

Women who labor with continuous doula support are more likely to have shorter labors and a spontaneous vaginal birth.

They are less likely to have:

- A negative experience
- An epidural or medical intervention
- Use of vacuum or forceps for baby
- A baby with a low APGAR score (high is better)

Communication happens through voice, which impacts the limbic system of the brain, the part affecting our emotions. Part of my job is to help you navigate rough waters. Ask. Chat. Hum. Scream. Tone. Sing. Use your voice! Be real.

There are three basic components key to an ideal birth:

RELAXATION, RHYTHM, AND RITUAL.

Find a way to be comfortable in the silence of your own inner being. Meditation and yoga can be lifesavers. Are they already part of your self-care practices?

Being able to look at each other face-to-face is ideal, without question.

Ponder this, please. Have you ever gone to the theatre and watched a performance or seen a show on TV that reached in, grabbed your heart, and brought emotion up and out, making you happy, feel good all over, cry or jump for joy?

Virtual impact! We may not be present, yet can we feel what is happening through a computer/TV screen!/ZOOM? Yes!

A doula from a distance is way better than no doula; I can promise you that!

Reading through phone/text communication about what is going on for you is key. I've done that. Long before Covid-19, I assisted a mom in my hometown with her labor by phone. She was not my client. We met briefly in the parking lot of my mother's assisted living facility. She had no one to support her birth. I had a nasty cold. When her contractions began, she called me, and we walked through her labor together. Guiding the mom from a distance to change positions (babies get stuck if we do nothing but lie on our backs) because the law of gravity matters. We walked verbally, jiggling, breathing and easing her stress, and more. It was awesome. She had a successful intervention-free delivery. Her humbling words afterward were, "I never could have done this without your help."

What terrified me and brought me to tears when doulas were 'locked-out' of labor and delivery with Covid is empowering me now.

DONA International has a saying: "Let's doula this!" And doula this, we will!

My mom taught us, "It ain't bragging if it's true!"

Doulas give new meaning to "I've got your back!"

I'm ready, with coping skills, as we walk through wherever you are emotionally, for four hours or thirty two! Teaching you and your partner everything I've learned fills my heart. I refuse to let a virus take back birth freedoms women have fought for. We fought for them, for our babies and ourselves, and by gosh, I am ready to do it again until we get back into the delivery room!

Learning techniques you can do for yourself, including acupressure, aromatherapy, birth balls positions, dancing, jiggling, Rebozos, warm compresses, and more, will change your birth experience!

Did you know hospital staff is often not allowed to use warm compresses due to liability issues? However, it is within my scope of practice as a doula, and babies love to follow warmth!

For clarity's sake, doulas do not 'turn' breech babies. I have taken Spinning Babies classes and think their work is fabulous. Facilitators guide. Babies and God, not necessarily in that order, decide the baby's position.

There are many tools, including laughter, which increase oxytocin levels in the body. Why do we want to increase oxytocin? It is your body's *natural* Pitocin without the toxic side effects for Momma and Baby.

Let's look at **Acupressure point GB 21**, midway between the high point of your shoulder and the juncture of your lowest cervical/highest thoracic vertebrae. ***Never*** use this point prior to actual labor, as it may possibly create an early start. Acupressure is exactly that, firm pressure to Momma's tolerance, not massage, not forcing. Let her guide you. The spot will be tender. Find it and hang out for at least three to five minutes. It can help stalled contractions.

Acupressure point K-1, beneath the ball of her foot, in the center, helps maintain calm during the labor of labor! Who knew? Chinese medicine knew ions ago that organs have emotional components. Kidneys hold fear. Imagine.

LESSON #1... FIND THE EARTH UNDERNEATH YOUR OWN TWO FEET.

Being grounded or centered is key to holding space. Feeling the earth helps.

Encouraging couples to walk the earth in silence, preferably barefoot, helps them feel a deeper-rooted, grounded space within themselves. Without using your hands, find the base of your spine. Feel it from the inside. Visually see and feel your coccyx, that little curled tail at the base of your spine. See it like a corkscrew winding its way into the core of Mother Earth. Feel it spinning deeper with every breath. When you feel it hit, curl that little monkey tail, and with a quick twist, lock your roots down solid.

Seems strange? Do it again.

If you find yourself off balance or unable to cope, come back to this exercise during birth. Anchor your own core into the deep core of the earth and know, "You've got this!"

When the mom you are supporting is struggling walk her through this using your own words. Use your strong-yet-gentle voice and guide her to feel the power of the earth coming up through her feet, simultaneously feeling her body anchored and safe.

If you're the support person present in the room with her, gently place your palm on her sacrum, the triangular bone just below her lowest vertebrae. The warmth of your hand will feel comforting and remind her she's not alone, which is a subtle, powerful tool.

Learning to 'hold space' for someone, whether in life or passing into life after this reality, is a privilege. It can be as easy or difficult as we choose to make it.

LESSON #2...LISTEN MORE THAN YOU TALK.

One key to birth support is much like any successful relationship.

Hear what your partner tells you. Validate it. Hear what she is saying without words. It is her story. Please let her tell it. Ask her what she needs, and listen with an open heart.

Honor and support what she feels in the moment. Birth plans are vital. They are plans which need to be flexible.

In labor, no one knows her body better than she does. No one.

Plan ahead of time for a key word for when she's really, really *done* with the natural route and may need an intervention. An epidural may make a difference.

No matter how much you both may have wanted a 100% natural birth, be gentle with yourselves.

Exhausted, excruciating, sobbing pain equates to suffering, which is far different from tired. Sometimes a mom can benefit from an intervention to rest if the labor has been long. It can also be what she needs to move forward and come back for round two and birth naturally!

Could the intervention be natural? Absolutely. Someone gently, methodically, slowly, washing your face can change your vitals.

What about a nice soak in a warm tub supported by noodles? Yep!

One key point when you and the birth mom are presented with any method of intervention, no matter how seemingly small, ask your provider if you have time to talk it over with each other and, "Is there another option?"

As simple as they may sound, those words are huge!

If the intervention is an emergency, you won't have an option.

If it's not an emergency, talk time may afford Mother Nature time to move things along with less invasiveness.

Can you tell I love this work?

Being an LMT specializing in trauma and PTSD with Myofascial Release for 23 years helped guide me into the birth world. My careers as an LMT and Doula are separate, and they are both an integral part of who I am.

Having my own son in 1969, without delivery support, led me into the birth world.

DOULAS AT A DISTANCE

The webinar offered by Penny Simkin in March 2020 re-enforced what I know as a doula, myofascial release therapist, and plain-ole human being. It takes a team, and every member is invaluable.

We can do this! Together from a distance, with your head held high, and by the time the dead leaves of winter burst into spring, hopefully, life will sift out this viral crisis and put us together face to face.

Thank you for searching for you and your unborn child.

Doulas do make a difference, and so can YOU!

Are you ready to add new tools to your birth journey?

References #1

World Health Organization. Clinical Management of Severe Acute Respiratory Infection (SARI) when COVID-19 Disease is Suspected. Geneva World Health Organization, 2020

2. Centers for Disease Control and Prevention, Interim Considerations for Infection Prevention and Control of Corona Virus Disease 2019 (COVID-19) in Inpatient Obstetric Healthcare Settings. https:/ cdc.gov/coronavirus/2019ncov/hcp/inpatient-obstetric healthcare-guidance.html Accessed March 31, 2020

Reference #2

*BREAST FEEDING MEDICINE

Volume 15, Number 5 2020

Mary Ann Liebart, Inc.

DOI 10.1089/blm.2020.29153.ams

** Alison Stuebe, MD MSc

President Academy of Breastfeeding Medicine

Linda Aileen Miller, LMT, CD(DONA) is the mother of two sons, and grandmother of two adorable grandsons. She is a Master-level facilitator who supports women, men and children who experience the mind-body effects of PTSD to heal and live joy-filled. Following a 32-year career with Delta Air Lines, she 'retired' three trips after 09/11/2001.

The consummate student, Linda is an expert-level John F. Barnes Myofascial Release specialist, with twenty-three years of experience in holistic bodywork. She is a Shamanic practitioner Certified in Imagine Breathing holistic breathwork.

With roots in Transpersonal Psychology, Linda is a Level 2 Holy Fire Reiki Master, Certified Sound Healer and continues her end-of-life support studies through The Institute for Birth, Breath and Death.

As a Certified Birth Doula, and a fierce advocate for the unborn with extensive training in supporting and holding space both in birth and for loss in pregnancy, her heart is filled with the miracles of life and death.

Linda offers individual bodywork and sound healing sessions, Doula services, books and programs, which help you dig deeper into authentic, holistic healing. To read more of Linda's birth work, and share your story in a safe space, please reach out now, @ Linda@lovingbirthjourneys.com

Writing is her passion. Helping her heal sharing on Medium.com, participating in Open Mic nights, and as an author, poet and storyteller she loves meandering through life's journey. "Who Is That Woman?" "Life Is The Muck, The Magic and The Miracles" and "Free-Fallin' into & out of Banana Puddin' Dreams" are her first three self-published works filled with fun, healing, laughter, lust and love.

Linda's RESOURCE pages are:

www.theinnerjourneyproductions.com

www.lovingbirthjourneys.com

Information regarding Doula trainings, and finding one near you, please check out:

www.dona.org

www.spinningbabies.com

www.birthbreathanddeath.com

CHAPTER 5

SELF-LISTENING

THE ONE-QUESTION PAUSE FOR A LIFE YOU LOVE

BY MEREDITH VAISH

MY STORY

Three years ago, I broke.

I took on an additional project at work I was excited about. I worked around the clock. I'm one of those people —perhaps like you—who's constantly busy, doing, performing, and taking care of others. Basically, I was constantly striving to prove myself.

You could call me a perfectionist, a high-achiever, super-reliable, whatever you named it; it came from an energy to please and prove so that I felt okay. My inner story reads something like this: I have value because look at all that I do! And if I'm not doing, I have no value.

Whew. That's exhausting!

After 16 years in a corporate job with huge responsibilities and even more duties at home as a mother, I burned out. And I burned out in a big way. You see, I not only never stopped to care for my emotional and spiritual self, but I also never nourished my physical body. Productivity was everything.

So when I was in charge of an important tech project at work, I put in insane hours. I wanted to be responsive, to contribute, and most importantly, to make things happen.

Yeah, you can see where this is going.

I worked around the clock and in places where my posture was less than supported, until one day, the ache and numbness in my shoulder, neck, and right arm was too hard to ignore. I couldn't lift my hand to work the mouse of my computer anymore, and I couldn't hold a fork or turn a doorknob.

I reluctantly reported this to my doctor, and she said, "This is a repetitive stress injury." She explained that it was from using my body repetitively, in constant tension, without taking breaks. And then she told me the worst news: "You're going to need to take a disability leave from work." [Gasp!]

Even though she was an expert telling me I needed a break, I still felt I could continue to deliver—*maybe I could get around my injury somehow and see this project through?* But the doctor insisted I rest and sent the official order to my manager.

Inside, I felt I was letting people down. I felt they would see me as lazy, or that I was making things up, or exaggerating just to get out of work. So I felt a huge amount of shame for having to take time for myself.

For my recovery, the doctor prescribed acupuncture. I went in for my first visit thinking, *the needles are going to be so scary.* The practitioner put in the needles, and it was surprisingly manageable, but then she lowered the lights and turned up the heater, and said, "Okay, I'm going to leave you for 20 minutes."

Whah?!

That was the first time I'd ever spent 20 minutes doing nothing. I was just laying there, being with my own thoughts, my feelings, and my pain. And oh, how the floodgates opened!

I began blubbering, doing the ugly cry, face-down in that massage table doughnut.

I kept thinking, *get yourself together. Stop crying. What's happening?* But I couldn't stop. The waves just kept coming, and I had no choice but to surrender to them.

I surrendered to the regret for having treated myself so poorly and to the sadness for criticizing myself so harshly. And I opened to the relief of finally receiving care, tenderness, and space.

I felt so grateful.

And that's when I understood I'm worth making room for. I'm worth taking time for. I'm worth listening to and caring for. That's when I decided to leave my corporate job to heal. Out of that rest and reflection came the mission for my company, Pause Box.

* * *

Fast-forward two years into my new business. It's mid-November, I enjoyed one of my most productive months ever, and instead of feeling elated, I felt exhausted.

I was doing #allthethings an entrepreneur should do—posting to social every day, engaging my network, cultivating community in my Facebook group, creating and launching new products, coaching clients, managing my team, taking online classes, and working with talented mentors and coaches.

I was looking at the success and thinking; *I need more. What if I pushed this offer, created this program, expanded this offering?* I got caught up in the endorphin rush of all that busyness. Like a runner's high, I tapped into my reserves and pushed myself further, pulling a couple of 16-hour workdays to meet a deadline. The event I prepped for was awesome, I was rewarded with great engagement and authentic connection, and I went into the weekend on a high fantasizing about all the ways to grow my success.

And then, the crash came.

That weekend, something turned off. I couldn't motivate myself to do my usual practices or check email and social, I indulged in wine and carbs, and I sat by myself in a funk. I was soul-level tired. I pushed myself to go for a hike—my usual remedy for funks. Usually, when I hike, I'm able to connect to my inner guidance, my intuition, my creator energy.

But, nope. Nothing.

By mile three, I realized I was in lockdown—a very scary state for a creative do-er and perpetual improver. I thought to myself, *maybe this is what writer's block feels like?* But it felt more than that. It felt like a whole-body block, a soul-block. I kept placing the call to Divine, but no one was picking up.

Then the shame came.

Oh, the irony. I teach Pause but couldn't prevent my own burnout. While doing #allthethings out there, I lost sight of how I wanted to feel in here. *I forgot to listen to myself. How did I let this happen?*

I used to think my tendency toward overworking was a result of being in corporate culture. But here I was, no cube in sight: just me, and my old patterns of proving, hustle, control, and over-effort. Thankfully, my work teaches me to honor what's showing up and not resist it. So I did that in a big way. I declared a pause for myself for the remainder of the year.

You heard that right—a two-month Pause.

All those big plans and ideas? I put them on hold. My ego was not happy with me, and I suffered non-stop assaults from my inner critic calling me *irresponsible, a quitter, weak,* and *an imposter.* I wanted to hide—and did, for a few days. I made a promise to myself that I wouldn't start any new programs until the new year and that I would use the time to write and rest and do only the things that restored me.

To launch the Pause officially, I arranged for two nights away at an Airbnb cottage in Half Moon Bay. I arrived with my favorite nonfiction books and poetry, an Oracle deck, crystals and stones, essential oils, candles, supplies for a personal Rip & Reveal session, plus groceries from Whole Foods. I didn't leave the cottage except to take beach walks. I rested, journaled, danced, and nourished myself. I also got clear that I wanted to create a new relationship with work and money, built on trust, play, relaxation, celebration, self-listening, and community.

And that's where I am today as I write this in December 2020. Slowly, my creative connection is returning. I'm inspired once again to show up. Transformation is messy, and being an entrepreneur means that my business is often my greatest teacher.

So why did I tell you the stories of my two most painful burnouts? Because it's easy to forget to put ourselves on the list. It's easy to get sucked into doing and achieving and, in the process, forget to nourish ourselves. And it's easy to overrule our inner voice when there's work to do! So, here's what I want you to know:

- When we listen to our innermost self, we receive soul-level nourishment.
- When we embrace our feelings and honor our inner inklings, our life dramatically improves.
- And the most obvious lesson of my experience is, don't wait. Don't wait for a forced pause to compel you to stop. Tune in regularly with an intentional pause.

Here's my wish for you as you pause and use the self-listening tool below. May this practice wake up that sleeping part of you and bring her to a loving space where you can nourish and care for her. Get quiet, ask, and then listen for what comes. Your power comes from listening to the messages from your innermost self. And when you listen to what you need the most (and honor it), your life unfolds in powerful ways. Are you ready to begin?

THE TOOL

Find a quiet place to sit with a journal and a pen. Get comfortable. Take three deep breaths to help you arrive. This tool is called The Repeating Question. It is exactly that. One question, asked many times, to help you access your inner knowing through deep, repetitive inquiry.

Your repeating question is: **"What do I most need right now?"**

This is an inquiry of inner needs, not outer ones. "I need a million dollars" or "I need answers to a business or relationship question" are not useful in terms of this exercise. Stick to what you most need in your immediate experience, in your body, and your feelings.

If you can, say the repeating question out loud and not just in your head. Write down any word that pops up. Don't censor it. Don't try and make sense of it. You are simply receiving the word and writing it down.

Next, say, "Thank You," and ask the question again: "What do I most need right now?" Keep going. Repeat this question a total of 15 times.

There may be a point where you freeze up or get caught in over-thinking. If that happens, just say, "Pass," and ask the question again. It's totally normal to repeat the same answer or to come up with words that are nonsensical or illogical. Just keep moving through the exercise. There is gold in honestly answering the question without the worry of doing it "right."

Initially, your words may feel surface-level (*I'm hungry, I need Advil*) that's fine.

Write it down and keep moving. When it comes to what you need, the answers are rarely linear. This exercise is a lot like life—the more you can follow your impulse, intuition, and gut-knowing, the better.

Now that you've asked yourself the repeating question at least 15 times (feel free to do more than that) look at your list of words. Circle the words that are feeling-type words or words that have a lot of energy to them. Pick one or two and ask yourself, "How can I honor this need today?"

This is the most important part of the exercise. By listening to what you most need and then taking action to give that to yourself, you are practicing self-honoring. When your intuition is honored, you grow your capacity to receive more. Receiving "more" is essential to creating a life of more freedom, joy, and impact.

An Example:

Let's say my repeating question revealed the following words: patience, breathe, stillness, take a walk, breath, affirm, tight, breathe, pressure relief, movement, butter, stretch, hurting, chocolate, be outside.

I circle the word "hurting" because it has the most energy for me. Next, I get curious. I feel "hurting" in my knuckle, but I know that it's also pointing to emotional pain. That feels true, so I go deeper into that feeling. As I sit with the feeling of "hurting," I'm reminded of feeling isolated and a little lonely. *What would bring my hurting comfort right now?* I ask myself. I picture snuggling up in a warm blanket, putting on an essential oil, maybe watching a romcom. I also think of reaching out to a good friend.

Your pause prescription is to honor what it is you're being told you most need. It can be a small action or an all-day affair. Most importantly, don't postpone taking your self-care until you have more time or it's convenient. The sooner you honor it, the sooner you build trust with your intuition. Treat yourself like a bestie. How would you urge them to honor their needs?

Taking time for this one-question Pause starts a virtuous cycle of tuning in, listening, and trusting. In doing this, you begin to create the life you love, one inspired action at a time.

Meredith Vaish is a recovering over-doer and chronic high-achiever who left corporate for a year-long 'soulbatical.' Thanks to what she learned during that Pause, she's now on a mission to help other creators, do-ers, and improvers break free from the overwhelm of being always-on.

Meredith speaks on the topic of Pause for clarity, intention, and connecting to your intuition so you can hear what's true for you, then take inspired action to create the life you love.

She offers retreats and programs that make space for possibility, create clarity, and inspire action. Join her in the Pausibility (Pause + Possibility) Facebook group for tips, tools, and high-vibe community. Meredith also offers breakthrough sessions to busy women looking to create clarity and momentum in their life and business.

Meredith lives in the San Francisco Bay Area with her husband and two teenage daughters. She can be found making soup, going outside to get away from her screen, customizing essential oil blends, and making good use of her foam roller. www.pauseboxco.com.

More resources are available, including an audio recording of the repeating question, at https://pauseboxco.com/resources/

CHAPTER 6

RESOLVING CELLULAR MEMORIES

YOUR ANCESTORS HAVE WAITED YOUR WHOLE LIFE FOR THIS MOMENT

AMY GILLESPIE, FOUNDER OF IRIGENICS™ ANCESTRAL EYE READING

MY STORY

Time stopped, and the room began to tilt as the retired navy commander implored, "Amy, you must continue this work. In years of therapy, we never talked about this." His voice quivered, "My God! You just explained in five minutes the answer we sought for years! I know…I know my son would be alive if we had ever had *this* conversation. Please. You must continue this work."

He made no attempt to wipe the brimming tears from his eyes. He gave me a nod as if to say; *you've been given your assignment, now be on about your business.*

My business. How had my life come to this moment of working in a cement-floored expo hall taking photographs of people's eyes, explaining their most detailed belief systems and earliest traumas, all in a matter of moments?

Wasn't it just two years earlier that I managed to rebuild a failed water treatment facility on the Arkansas River?

I had a lifetime of solving people's problems: as an aid worker in Africa, insurance adjuster, systems performance manager, and as a friend. But what of my own problems? Had I ever resolved my struggle with self-esteem? My inability to hear "I love you" from my parents? My feeling of not being good enough? That I should have been born a boy?

Luckily, I'm one of the few who have made this rocky journey through life to finally understand the missing piece of my story. The piece that my mind had understood, but my heart and cellular memory had always refused to let go of.

I was a mistake. It was my fault. It was because of me that the trajectory of my parent's lives had changed forever. I'd always known it. My adopted parents explained it to me from my youngest years. My birth parents were too young to raise me and placed me up for adoption with a loving desire that I be raised with a good family, and I was.

As a child, I only wanted to find my birth family. With my full Barbie doll case and Mom's checkbook, I ran away from home, determined to get to Iowa to find my biological family. I was certain that once I crossed the state line, I would have immunity and the ability to locate my birth parents.

What I didn't discover until decades later is that my origin was within me. Every time I screamed, "Let me up! Let me go! Let me out!" I relived the exact dynamics of my ancestor's experience and re-infused the belief that *sibling rivalry was still a threat* to our genetic line.

The sickening feeling that turned over my stomach when I realized I'd overdrawn my bank account was the exact same chemical response of my ancestors (in their time) realizing *the money was gone.*

As I lamented, *why didn't I wait?!* I was repeating their regret and the same chemical reaction they experienced when they realized they had done something that overdrew their resources when they bemoaned. *Why didn't I wait?!*

As I took my first corporate job in the city, I could never have imagined I interviewed in the same office that my birthmother interviewed in 18 years earlier (even though it was three hours away from where either of us grew up).

As I challenged my adopted parents for years, wanting to change my middle name from Louise to Laroy, I had no idea I was seeking the name of the king that my ancestors fought under in the battle of Hastings and that the battle scroll hung on my birthfather's wall. My birthfather developed a system of accurately reading fingerprints, as I was developing a system of reading eyes.

Decades of piecing together clues revealed the amazing and rich history of my origin, of my ancestors' repeated patterns and traumas playing out in my own life from the time of my conception. I had only to look at my life experiences to find the experiences of my forebearers.

Each time I exclaimed with emotion, it was as if their words were coming through me (in their accent, in their foreign language) as an opportunity to reaffirm or disavow if each situation was still a threat to our genetic line, or if it was no longer a threat in this brave new world of today.

I soon figured out that this situation of not being able to hear, "I love you" (and the other aspects of cellular memory) were not just facets of an adopted or foster child, but that we all have the opportunity to revisit and resolve early cellular memories.

I often see this pattern of feeling unwanted in children conceived during a military furlough or just prior to active duty, as happened to the retired navy admiral. In my experience, the dynamics of our parents' experience of their pregnancy with us repeats every two to four, or three to five generations, often going back for hundreds of years.

In this moment, I think of babies who have been conceived during the COVID-19 pandemic and how many mothers (and fathers) are experiencing fears of being pregnant (an ancestral repeat of pregnancies during other pandemics, such as the 1918 Spanish Flu). These fears can culminate in the child as a feeling of not being wanted or that there is something wrong with them.

Every day, we all have an opportunity to resolve our ancestral traumas and to embrace the magic of who we were born to become.

Amy, you must continue this work, helping others to understand the rest of their story. To finally recognize and understand their cellular memory imprints that happened in-utero, so they can resolve and resume the life they were born to live.

THE TOOL

If you prefer to listen to a free audio version of this guided visual exercise, please go to my resource link: https://irigenics.com/guidedexercise/

Prepare a safe, open floor space. You will want 10-12 feet (about the length of a small bedroom) for this exercise. You should have enough width to imagine an adult walking on each side of you.

You may want to journal or record your experience at the end.

NOTE TO THE READER

If you don't know your biological parents, you know they existed one year before you were born. Just imagine the best of who they were for this visualization.

If you've had challenging relations with your parents, remember this exercise is only for the time before you were born, before you had any experience of them. Imagine their happiest essence for this visualization.

If you are ready to play the recording, go here: https://irigenics.com/guidedexercise/

On the floor, create an imaginary timeline of one year plus a day, with enough comfortable room at the end of that line to turn around.

Does it run from left to right? Right to left? Or in front of you going forward?

Physically, stand at the beginning of your timeline, with enough room on each side of you to imagine holding hands with each parent as you walk its length. This is a loving visualization, and you are standing at the beginning (one year before your birth). They may or may not know each other, may or may not be married, and may or may not have other children. At this time, you are just focusing on their essence. Breathe.

Does it feel better to have your mother on your left? Or your father? If you need to swap their positions, do that, and check again. Does it feel correct now? Give your body a deep, cleansing breath and gently shake your hands freely to clear your energy.

Gently close your eyes and breathe deeply. Now imagine each of your parents taking your hand. Take a few minutes to just breathe with them.

This was before you were born, and before you were conceived. They were just people, living their lives as you are today. Even if you don't know them or anything about them, you know they existed a year before you were born, and you're just standing there, breathing with them.

Take a moment to note the feeling of your hand in each of theirs. If you feel any resistance, gently remind yourself this is one year before you were born. You have no experience of them yet. You are feeling their best essence before you ever met them in this exercise.

Now, gently turn your attention to the parent on your left. Breathe with your focus on them for a few moments. Allow yourself to feel their happy place as if their hand was transmitting it to you: their favorite color, fragrance, sound, music, taste, and happiest memories. Even if you don't know them or their favorite things, it's okay to just receive what they're sending you as if it's all perfectly true. Enjoy the wonderment they are feeling in recalling their very favorite experiences.

Spend a few moments with them. This time and space are for connecting with their most joyful and happy times. If anything comes that doesn't feel right, just bless it and let it go for another time. Hold their hand as you do this. You are giving them permission to feel their favorite moments and share that feeling openly with you. Give them the gift of a few moments of love, enjoyment, and happiness. Hold their energy in love and light. This is all before you were born, before you met them, when they were just a person doing what they do.

Gently bring your energy back to yourself, allowing them to hold onto those wonderful impressions while still holding your hand. Take a few deep breaths from head to toe.

Now, gently turn your attention to your parent on the right. Breathe, with your focus on them for a few moments. Allow yourself to feel their happy place as if their hand was transmitting it to you: their favorite color, fragrance, sound, music, taste, and happiest memories. Even if you don't know them or their favorite things, it's okay to just receive what they are sending, as if it's all perfectly true. Enjoy the wonderment they are feeling in recalling their very favorite memories.

Spend a few moments with them. This time and space are for connecting with their most joyful and happy times. If anything comes that doesn't feel right, just bless it and let it go for another time. Hold their hand as you do this. You are giving them permission to feel their favorite moments and share that feeling openly with you. Give them the gift of a few moments of love, enjoyment, and happiness. Hold their energy in love and light. This is all before you were born, before you met them, when they were just a person doing what they do.

Gently bring your energy back to yourself, allowing them to hold onto those wonderful impressions while still holding your hand. Take a few deep breaths from head to toe.

Breathe slowly and fully for a few moments as you infuse yourself with a color you love, a fragrance, sound, music, taste, and happiest experiences. If anything comes that doesn't feel right, just bless it and let it go for another time. This time and space are for connecting your most joyful and happy moments. Hold your parents' hands as you do this. Infuse them with the most wonderful experiences of your life. Load them up with the best of the best you have enjoyed and experienced and the hope of all that is yet to come as you continue forward.

Now, imagine filling the timeline in front of you with your favorite color, your favorite fragrance, your favorite sound or music. Imagine spreading that essence out, filling the room. It feels particularly inviting to you as you stand at the start of your timeline.

Smile to each parent, reassuring your hold on each of their hands as you take your first step forward, the three of you together, three months before your conception, one year before your birth. Each of you is filled with your personal joys and favorites. Each of your parents is filled with their best experiences and memories.

Hold their hands, breathe, and whisper (aloud or silently), "I've got you. We're going through this together." This walk is about your time of life. Even if your parent is deceased, they're holding your hands as you go. Step into your timeline one year before your birth. Take small, purposeful steps for each month, eleven months before your birth.

Take a moment to bless your ancestors and their amazing gifts as you take these steps. Bless your parents for your connection to them. Walk slowly and purposefully. Fill yourself with love for those ancestors who had impossible journeys and decisions, and exhale that energy with love and light. Imagine the magnitude of your ancestors, who created the next generation and the next, all the way to infusing your parents with their best gifts and talents, that came to you, and live on through you now.

Ten months before. Embrace gratitude that your parents gave you the link to the very best of your ancestors and your inherent gifts and talents.

Gently walk your parents through the full term of their pregnancy with you, brushing away any challenging memories (with love and light) for a later time and place.

As you reach the current moment of your life, slow yourself and stop. Still holding their hands, raise your head, and imagine your bright, graceful, joyous future with hope and love and knowing that the deep resonance within you is that of your ancestors. Their greatest gifts, strengths, abilities, and intentions live on through you and your future.

Nobody has ever walked our planet with the same ancestral connections as you, and no one else ever will. Embrace that for a moment as you breathe with your parents holding their hands. They are the link to your most beautiful and gifted ancestors.

Look to the parent on your left. Thank them, still holding your connection in love and light, for bringing you to this future that awaits you. Feel gratitude in your heart as you recognize that you have also walked them through this timeline to the moment of your birth. Move your energy up to your heart, establishing a heart connection as you gently let go of their hand. Breathe with them a bit longer, embracing that love.

Gently bring your energy back to your center. Take a couple of deep head-to-toe breaths and look to the parent on your right.

Thank them, still holding your connection in love and light, for bringing you to this future that awaits you. Feel gratitude in your heart as you recognize that you have also walked them through this timeline to the moment of your birth. Move your energy up to your heart, establishing a heart connection as you gently let go of their hand. Breathe with them a bit longer, embracing that love.

Take one more step forward, lovingly releasing your parents' energy.

Gently bring your energy back to your center, and bring your hands up to your heart. Take a couple of deep, cleansing breaths, and imagine your ancestors for a moment.

As you are one step in front of the timeline, whisper a thank you to the thousands of lives that have come before you to bring you to this moment. Thank them for being your spiritual sponsors, bringing you their many generations of skills and gifts every day. Gently open your eyes and remember:

In every moment of this life,

Forever the world is changed

Because you are here

And your ancestors are with you

Gently bring your awareness back to the present moment where you can now record your experience.

Amy Gillespie Dougherty, founder of Irigenics™ Ancestral Eye Reading and CLARA (Children's Lives Are the Responsibility of All).

Life handed Amy every external blessing, a loving adopted family growing up on a farm in the rural Midwest. It also handed her every internal torment of feeling unwanted, that everything was her fault, that she should have been born a boy, or not born at all. She ran away from home as a child and away from life as an adult.

Questions of her origin haunted her. *Who am I?! Where did I come from? What nationality am I? Why do I have two different colored eyes?*

At age 19, she met her birth mother and her maternal family, which unveiled the unbelievable synchronicities of genetics unknown. It wasn't until she returned from six years in Africa, creating survival skills for children, that she realized how current self-esteem tools had not resolved her core issue of not being able to hear, "I love you."

A chance meeting with a retired Navy Admiral convinced her she needed to look deeper into her life experience of contemplating her own suicide more than once by the age of 25.

She found her answers in the most unlikely place, in the world of her ancestors. Having met her birth mother at age 19 and her birth father in her fifties, she had a rare opportunity to delve into nature vs. nurture, discovering the most unbelievable synchronicities between her life and her biological family.

She began to unravel the epigenetic treasure map in our eyes that revealed how even her adopted life experiences handed her the historical markers of her ancestors. Today she brings just one cutting-edge, self-discovery tool in this exercise, resolving the cellular memories you have from your time in-utero. To learn more about her books, click here: https://irigenics.com/project/my-books/

CHAPTER 7

NUTRITIONAL DETOX

READY TO STOP FEELING SICK AND TIRED OF BEING SICK AND TIRED?

DR. ELLE PROVENCHER DTN, RND-BC, FIFHI, AEMP, RM, CH

MY STORY

I was on vacation with my husband in Jamaica for a week of good food and cocktails. I left the island fitting in my jeans, and then ten days after returning home, I gained 20 pounds, and my pants no longer fit. I blew up like a codfish! I was craving bread and anything with sugar. I'm a gym rat and watch what I eat most of the time. This was a new experience craving these foods. Even though I did not cave in and consume the snacks, the weight, the bloat, and the clouded head began.

After a visit to my doctor and $2000 of blood work (I had no medical insurance at the time), they could not give me a reason for my symptoms. It was so frustrating. What the heck!

The doctors had no idea what was wrong. This led me to a local massage therapist who focused on nutrition. Upon arriving, I filled out an intake form that prompted me to answer questions.

Do you suffer from constant fatigue, head tension, digestion issues, weight gain, cloudy thoughts, poor sleep, muscle pain, sensitivity to odors, or water retention? Yikes, that sounded like me since I returned from vacation!

The kind therapist explained to me, "Those are signs that it's time to clean up the toxins in your body. You may be suffering from a condition called Candida. Candida is the overabundance of yeast in the body. Not a yeast infection, but that too could be a symptom. When you're feeling unwell, the body is inflamed, and that causes all sorts of havoc. Basically, the Candida gets to run amok throughout your entire body."

Low and behold, after completing the intake form, I scored high on the symptoms of having Candida. Lucky me! Before this, I had no idea what Candida was. I was singing the old song, *Candida*, by Tony Orlando and Dawn in my head. That was my only reference!

As the practitioner explained Candida more to me, the aha part of my brain woke up. I was not on medications, but I experienced being on birth control in my early 20's and was given doses of antibiotics throughout my early life. I also had anesthesia when I had my wisdom teeth out. Those antibiotics allowed the yeast to start to hibernate in my body. I ate well normally and took care of my health. My husband was about to learn that his poor eating and consumption of high sugar foods was feeding the yeast in his body. She let me know that he was most likely full of Candida and was a contributor to mine. You can share this with your partner during intercourse. My over-abundance of yeast jumped into high gear with the rapid increase of sugar from cocktails, beach food, and many nights in the hot tub. Who knew!?

FYI

Foods that feed Candida include all forms of sugar, including fruit, yeast, dairy, red meat, bread, alcohol, and pastries. If these foods make up a great deal of your diet, there is a great opportunity for you to reduce and possibly eradicate your Candida.

Antibiotics never truly leave the body. The body adapts to antibiotics. When you were young, amoxicillin probably worked well on you, but as you grew, it no longer worked. The germs that died off from the amoxicillin were released from your body, but the stronger germs stayed alive and adapted not to be killed by amoxicillin again. The strong stayed strong to survive. So now, even a Z-Pak may not pack a punch for you. We have come to a time in traditional medicine where scientists are unable to create a stronger antibiotic. But that is a whole other topic!

Back to Candida and what I did to eradicate the buggers out of me!

I was invited to partake in a natural approach to building up my immune system using a nutritional program and a guided foods diet to clean up my health.

It was not a hard program, but it was a cool approach to health that led me on my path to becoming a Doctor of Traditional Naturopathy. I learned that the body is an amazing thing. When you feed it what it requires, health and wellness can be achieved.

My program began by introducing an eating program that used herbology and supplementation to strengthen my body. I still use this ideology in all my programs for my patients.

I learned about supplements that I could understand: A daily herbal vitamin, specific calcium to help my body get in the correct PH balance (yes, that is a thing!), and antioxidant and herbal supplements to support all my organs and to relax my mind and body. It also included a specific fiber and probiotic that together would assist in eradicating the Candida. The detoxification herbs were the magic with the diet that made this key to overcoming Candida.

Beginning the program was not hard at all. It was getting the idea past my husband! As we had been still in our honeymoon phase, "relations" had to be adjusted. Who knew that "relations" could transfer Candida from one partner to another? After vacation, my body reached a point of stress from that quick shift into a lifestyle that a Rockstar could appreciate for a week. That fun week of sunshine, dancing, Pina Coladas, and lots of grilled cheese sandwiches and French fries on the beach did me in. Not my usual diet for sure!

As I stated before, my husband was a milk drinking, white bread eating, soda, junk food, and ketchup loving guy! These are all the foods that make Candida do a little dance and jump for joy! These foods feed Candida and set you up for the super trap. Candida makes you crave what keeps them alive. Sneaky!

My husband wasn't on board with me, putting the kibosh on our "relations" by having to wear "protection." As a good husband, he decided to go on the program with me. Yes, he had to give up the foods that were giving him some health challenges. He was on blood pressure medication and Nexium for his acid reflux, which also contributed to his candida infestation. He was starting to bloat, and his belly was often uncomfortable.

This was the beginning of our road to better health!

We began the program by changing our diet and following the supplementation plan that supported our body, not just putting a band-aid on it. It was getting to the root of the problem.

The elimination of sugar in all forms, yeast, dairy, red meat, caffeine, and alcohol, became the focus for our 30-day program. Don't panic if you're considering how to do a program like this! Reach out to me by following my info at the end of this chapter! I will be happy to guide you through a program. I have been nutritionally detoxing people and families for over 20 years, and this program is still my personal favorite. It can also help relieve the symptoms of fibromyalgia, Lyme's disease, obesity, constipation issues, and many more.

Throughout the 30 days, our health practitioner checked in with us daily to support us in our healing and answer any questions. I still follow this format with any of the patients that choose to engage in this program.

We ate every day except for a three-day liquid part of the cleanse. At first, that brought up all sorts of fear! But it was super easy! We weren't hungry and managed it easily. The liquid part of the cleanse tastes like lemonade. It was a mixture that you may know as the Master Mix (without the cayenne). This mixture is one that the body recognizes as fuel, and the body can readily use without chewing. During this time, your body gets to work on healing itself, instead of having to spend a lot of time and energy digesting food. It's as easy as sipping the mix all day in addition to drinking 64 oz of water a day. You will have enough calories to live! I likened it to having an IV drip in the hospital; your body uses the IV mix as fuel.

The Candida cleanse advised to only drink distilled water to leach out the Candida and impurities. We drank half of our body weight in ounces each day. Pure water is a magical substance from the Earth that our bodies require! The consumption of the water helps the body not to be dehydrated. It also helps how the herbal compounds heal the body and allow the colon to do its job. Think of your colon as a huge septic tank that needs to be cleaned of debris and toxins. Drinking the correct amount of water each day and consuming fiber is an opportunity for everyone. Eliminating negative thoughts, behaviors, and toxins are part of how the colon releases. Drink the water, let the colon work. Think of a "Drano" commercial. Remember that pipe all full of crud? That is your colon, full of that stuff; leftover medicine, antibiotics, undigested food, and parasites—all sorts of yuck. Doing a nutritional cleanse that respects and builds the body helps the colon and you. What you may not know, clean blood flows through your colon and gets dirty. It then flows up through your body and brain on its way back to the heart and lungs to be filtered. Can you see how the clean blood gets dirty and drags all that nasty stuff throughout your body? When your blood is dirty, the body can only filter out so much before inflammation and problems happen in the organs.

John Wayne died with 40 pounds of undigested meat in his colon. Remember how big his belly was? That was all that meat rotting away and creating gas and challenges in his body. He became forgetful, and yes, he was full of Candida. Don't let this be you!

Back to the cleanse.

The program recommended incorporating the candida legal foods list for six days and followed with two days of vegetarian eating throughout the month. Then three days (up to ten if you'd like) of the liquid mixture. Then the liquid cleanse fast is broken by introducing raw veggies for the day. Back to vegetarian (vegetables and grains only) for a day, and then continuing to consume protein, vegetables, and grains. On day 16, cooked fruit is added to the mix. A piece of raw fruit would have too much sugar and can cause a belly ache. Why cooked fruit? Cooking the fruit takes the sugar level down and makes it easier to digest. Some people find out that one of their favorite fruits may be causing digestion issues and inflammation. Each day for a week, new cooked fruit is introduced to see if there are any reactions. How did I cook the fruit? I put it in hot oatmeal each morning, and voila! That took the excess sugar off. In the last week of the program, we add back in the fresh fruit and bread with yeast for testing. This is done to see how the body responds to these foods to see any reactions or negative responses. By now, the Candida should be eradicated. If it is not, you can repeat days 7-16.

The diet was a huge piece of the healing. I can tell you, though, the specific herbal compounds made the difference in getting the Candida out.

Yes, I experienced a healing crisis some days, and low and behold, I released a few parasites that were hiding in my GI tract. Parasites can look like white, wet yarn or string in the stool. Better out than in! The days of feeling a little crappy far outweighed the symptoms I had before knowing I had a way to feel better. I worked every day of the program, as did my husband. We were not confined to the bathroom. Remember, we were building the health of the body in a kind and gentle manner. A Roto-Rooter approach is not so good for the body.

Some other interesting body mechanics can happen during the cleanse—armpits smelling like vegetable soup or sugar cookies (that's the yeast coming out!). A coated tongue (turns white) means more yeast is coming out! Sometimes a skin breakout occurs. Yes, more yeast is coming out! Bad breath can occur (elimination of toxins out of the lungs). The stool may be pumpkin spice in color and have white globs on it. That's Candida with dairy! Give the body what it needs to clean house and it will!

On to our results! I dropped those pesky 20 pounds of Candida that filled my body. My body was healthier, stronger, and leaner than before I left for Jamaica. My husband was able to stop taking his Nexium, and his blood pressure meds were lowered.

Of course, results vary. But I can promise you that you can get your body feeling better if you follow the program and do not cheat.

I do the same program two to three times a year to strengthen my immune system and revitalize my cells.

If you're ready to stop feeling sick and tired of being sick and tired, let's lock arms and let me help get you on the path to wellness.

THE TOOL

This self-screening for a Candida or Yeast Problem is provided for general information only and is not intended to be used for self-diagnosis without the advice and examination of a health professional.

- Do you feel tired most of the time? Does fatigue alter your lifestyle?
- Do you suffer from intestinal gas, or abdominal bloating, or discomfort?
- Do you crave vinegar, sugar, breads, beer, or other alcoholic beverages?

- Are you bothered by bowel disorders, constipation, diarrhea, or alternating constipation/diarrhea?
- Do you suffer from anxiety, depression, panic attacks, or mood swings?
- Are you often irritable, easily angered, anxious, or nervous?
- Do you have trouble thinking clearly, or suffer memory loss (particularly short-term memory loss)?
- Are you ever faint, dizzy or light-headed?
- Do you have muscle aches or take more than 24 hours to recover from normal activity?
- Without a change in diet, have you had weight gain and not been able to lose the weight no matter what you have tried?
- Does itching or burning of the vagina, rectum, or prostate bother you, or have you experienced a loss of sexual desire?
- Do you have a white or yellow fuzzy coating on your tongue?
- Have you had athletes foot, ringworm, jock itch, or other chronic fungus infection of the skin or nails?
- Does exposure to perfumes, insecticides, new carpeting, or other chemical smells bother you?
- Have you at any time in your life taken "broad spectrum" antibiotics, tetracyclines (Sumycin, Panmycin, Vibromygin, Minocin), Penicillin, Ampacillin, etc.?
- Are you using birth control pills or shots, or have you ever used birth control pills or shots?
- Are you on synthetic hormones?
- Have you ever taken steroid drugs? These are often used for allergies, asthma, respiratory problems, and injuries (cortisone, prednisone, decadron, etc.).

RATE YOUR CANDIDA PROBABILITY: How many questions were a yes?

12 or more: Very high

7 to 11: High

5 to 6: Moderate

0 to 4: Low

Dr. Elle Provencher

Board Certified Doctor of Traditional Naturopathy,

Board Certified Doctor of Natural Medicine,

Bachelor of Science- Holistic and Bariatric Nutrition,

Fellow with The Institute of Human Individuality,

Advanced Energy Medicine Practitioner,

Reiki Master (Usui/Karuna Ki),

Certified Hypnotist, Author,

National Wellness Speaker and Advocate for Natural Health Solutions

Wife, Mom, Grandmother, Sister, Aunt, Great Aunt, Friend, Cat Mom

I offer natural health solutions to enhance your health and wellness in a kind, professional, and respectful manner. Focusing on an individualized mind-body-soul approach, I care about YOU!

Come visit my resource page for a complimentary Candida Screening Test and guided meditation for stress relief.
www.wellspringnaturalhealthsolutions.com/resources

If you discover that you are interested in a nutritional detoxification program, please contact me at dr.elle@icloud.com to request a complimentary 15 min wellness consultation and learn more about how I can assist you with your wellness.

It has been such an honor being part of this series of self-healing. I was featured in Chapter 15: Self-Hypnosis With Your Eyes Open, in *The Ultimate Guide to Self-Healing Volume 3.*

I hope that you found value in these books! They offer great healing and know that you have begun your journey of better health just by picking up this book.

Who you are makes a difference in the world! Keep on being YOU!

Namaste,

Dr. Elle

www.WellspringNaturalHealthSolutions.com

www.BeWellWithDrElle.com

www.MicroFrequencyDr.com

CHAPTER 8

HABITS THAT HEAL

TAP INTO YOUR PERSONAL ENERGY TO CREATE CHANGES THAT LAST

LAURA BUCKLEY, MS, RD, LDN

MY STORY

My client (let's call her Sally) and I chatted for a few minutes about the pressure she felt around "getting healthy" and all the things she'd tried before. We talked about the frustration, guilt, and shame she experienced when she "failed" at another "tried and true lifestyle habit."

And then I asked her, "What do *you* want?"

That's when the tears started to flow. And the answer:

"I don't know."

Just writing this brings tears to my eyes. Partly because of the amount of pain I've witnessed with my clients who have a similar story, partly because of my own journey along this path, and partly because this pain that feels almost universal is completely unnecessary.

We've become so conditioned around what it means to be "healthy" with a persistent emphasis on weight loss. And our minds are flooded with things we need to do to "earn" our wellbeing (primarily focused on rigid diets and unobtainable amounts of exercise).

In other words, we receive so many messages about what we're *supposed to do* that we feel out of touch with what we *want to do.*

We see it in the media; we hear it from those around us; and the same story is on repeat in our minds:

If I could just lose weight.

If I could just get to the gym four times a week.

If I could just stop eating all the carbs.

Then what?

Then I would feel happy. Healthy. Confident. Well.

But that is what I call "The broken promise of thinness."

The messages are all around us: If we want to find love and prosperity, if we want to feel free and safe, we must also strive for thinness.

We're taught that striving for fitness and achieving thinness will create a greater sense of worth.

We're encouraged to fit in, not to be "too much," or "too loud," and certainly not "too big."

And not only are those messages keeping us quiet and confused: they don't deliver on their promise.

So, when we work to achieve them and then we don't get the outcomes we (maybe subconsciously) hoped for, our bodies' push back and old habits slide back in; and we're left feeling even worse than where we started.

I remember the moment I fully realized this. I sat at my kitchen table in tears, reflecting on all the diets I tried, all the counting and tracking and planning I did, and all the education I had.

I was a registered dietitian for over ten years at this point, and I *still* didn't feel like I had control over my own body. I felt like a fraud.

Then it came to me in a moment of clarity:

What I actually desired wasn't thinness; it's what I was taught to believe the thinness would bring.

I was searching for confidence and connection and to feel valued and loved. And I was fighting with my own body and ignoring my needs to try to get there. I was disconnecting from myself to try to feel more connected!

I listened to all of the guidance coming from outside of myself instead of trusting my body and tuning into what *it* had to say.

This was my turning point.

It felt like going back to square one as I reflected on all the lies I believed about wellbeing and all the systems and approaches I tried for myself and my clients that didn't work. I had to unlearn what it means to be "healthy."

But through that process, I redefined my personal version of wellbeing and created processes and programs to help others do the same using tools that truly support people on their journey toward feeling safe and at home in their bodies.

It all starts here:

What if you don't need to change your body to feel good in it, to partner with it?

And more importantly:

What if your worth has nothing to do with your weight or your wellbeing?

What if it's inherently yours. Now. Today. And you can embrace it right here in this moment?

Let's get back to Sally:

I always have my clients bring a few goals to our first session. Sally brought three:

- "I want to stop worrying about food all of the time."
- "I want to *want* to exercise."
- "I want to stop the all or nothing mindset."

We discussed each one. We explored them, and we dug a little deeper. Under the surface, we found different goals. Goals that felt more meaningful and real for Sally:

- "I want to eat in a way that feels healthy AND easy."
- "I want to be less irritable and have more fun."
- "I want to feel like myself again."

And as we dug even deeper, we found a common theme to all of them: The desire for peace and calm.

From that awareness, we were able to reconnect Sally with her body and intuition to guide her healing process and move toward wellbeing.

I had Sally recall when she felt that feeling of peace and calm she was searching for. Then, I guided her in using her imagination to experience those feelings again.

As I watched her visualize and imagine and play with what it is to feel peace and calm, I saw a smile spread across her face.

Her shoulders relaxed, and she began to breathe more deeply than she had in a while.

Without making a single change in her lifestyle, she was able to feel at ease.

And from that place, I asked her, "What will support your wellbeing in this moment?"

The answer was so much clearer:

- "I want to dance."
- "I want a break from technology."
- "I want to rest."

And because she knew exactly what she wanted and listened to her body on what to do to get there, she was, for the first time in a long time (maybe ever), excited to take steps toward wellbeing.

In a few short weeks, she reported feeling more confident, having more kindness with her body, and even improving her relationship with her mother. It's all connected. The way we partner with our bodies is reflected in other partnerships in our lives as well!

When we look outside ourselves for the "right" habits to support our wellbeing, we frequently take action from a place of fear, shame, or not-enoughness. We give our power over to others claiming to be the "experts" on what our bodies need. And the process ends up feeling hard and disempowering.

But, the truth is, *you* are the expert in what you need. When you tap into your most authentic desires and reconnect with your body, the path toward wellbeing becomes clear and, before you even make a single change, the results start to feel inevitable.

Sally's story is not unique, but, as is true for so many people, she felt completely alone in it because she was trying to work through it on her own, struggling in silence.

With a few tools, you can embark on your own self-healing journey (which I suppose you already believe as you are holding this book in your hands).

If you can see yourself in this story, read on, my friend. This tool is for you.

Your turn!

You can experience the exact same energy, excitement, and awareness that Sally did by following a few simple steps that will help you:

- Tune back into your (unique, personal, and super-authentic) desires
- Reconnect with your body and listen to it for guidance
- Feel energized to lead a lifestyle that feels true to you (and not the result of a narrow, socially conditioned definition of "health")

Ready? Let's go!

THE TOOL

For complimentary worksheets and a guided audio version of this tool, please visit: https://www.laurabuckleycoaching.com/ug-resource-page/

STEP ONE: EXPLORE YOUR GOALS.

Jot down a few goals. Don't overthink them. They don't have to be "right." They're just a starting point, an entry point into that beautiful brain of yours. So, whatever comes to mind first, let's use that.

Side note on goals: Commonly held beliefs and teachings around goal-setting are not useful when it comes to health and wellbeing. While goals that are specific, measurable, and time-bound may be helpful in the work-place or in other outcomes-based environments, that type of goal is not as high-value when it comes to wellbeing. What's more important is that we tap into the underlying desires because wellbeing is not an outcome; it's a journey. That said, traditional goals are a great starting point to get to the heart of your desires, as we will do in this exercise.

Let's take each of your goals through a process of exploration to get to the underlying desire associated with each one. You may have to do this a few times to really get to the roots, and, as with anything new, your brain may resist. That's Okay! Just stick with it. It's worth it.

Ask yourself, "Why do I want this goal?" And when you hear the answer, write it down. If possible, go with the first thing you hear. That's likely your intuition talking to you.

Then ask yourself, "Why do I want that (whatever the above answer was)?"

Another answer and another ask: "Why is that important?"

Your desire for a certain outcome has many layers. You may have to dig a little to get to the root of it so you can see it clearly.

You'll know you have your most meaningful desire when the answer makes you feel giddy or makes you cry. Either way, it's awesome.

Repeat this process for any additional goals that you set at the beginning of the exercise.

Once you've worked through each of your goals, take a look and see if you can find a common theme. This common theme is generally a feeling.

Some of the most common feelings I see emerge are:

- Joy
- Freedom
- Peace
- Acceptance
- Confidence

Whatever it is for you, write it down.

STEP TWO: VISUALIZE SUCCESS

Place your feet on the floor, relax any tension in your body, and close your eyes (or rest your gaze down if that's more comfortable). Imagine yourself experiencing the feeling you identified above.

Recall a time you felt that way before and revisit the feeling.

Tap into it. Hold onto it. Savor it. Enjoy it. Experience it as though it is real for you today, because it is.

Ask yourself the following questions:

- How is your life different when you're experiencing that feeling?
- How are YOU different?
- How are you holding your body?
- What is the expression on your face?
- Where do you feel it in your body?
- How does it feel in your body?

The brain is incredibly persuaded by imagination. If you can imagine the outcomes and feelings you desire, your brain and body will experience it as reality, and therefore, it *is* your reality.

When you want to experience an emotion, this process is always available to you!

STEP THREE: ALLOW THIS EMOTIONAL ENERGY TO GUIDE YOU

Emotional energy is powerful. When you generate emotions that you desire, it actually allows the brain to expand perception, increase creativity, and improve problem-solving skills. How cool is that?

Step two guided you to generate the emotional energy you desire. This is the same energy you will now use to fuel your journey toward wellbeing.

Remember that emotional energy is always available to you when you take the time to tap into it and create it from your very powerful imagination.

Let's tap into the wisdom inside of that emotional experience to guide your way forward.

When you are in that energetic place, ask yourself, "What do I need to do today to support my wellbeing in this moment?"

And listen for the answer.

Some of the most common answers my clients hear are:

"Rest."

"Stretch."

"Move."

"Dance."

"Go outside."

Whatever you hear, try to make time to do it, even if it's just for a few minutes. The more you listen to your body and honor what it asks for, the more it will talk to you (kind of like any other partnership)!

A key element is having faith that what your body tells you it needs is what it actually needs. We've been hearing other people's guidance on how to care for our bodies for so long that it can be hard to listen to ourselves, especially when our bodies ask for something very different from what we've been taught is "healthy."

I often say we have to connect, listen, and trust:

Connect with our desires, our emotions, and our bodies.

Listen to what the inner voice has to say.

Trust that over time, the guidance from within will create a greater sense of wellbeing.

The more you listen and trust, the stronger the connection will be, and you'll find yourself in a self-fueled cycle that gets you closer and closer to a beautiful experience of health and wellbeing.

Bonus Tip!

The human brain loves a bit of recognition. When you go through this process to partner with your body to take action toward your wellbeing, take the time to celebrate yourself!

YOU DID IT! You took the steps to move toward a well-aligned approach to your wellbeing.

Cheer yourself on. It creates the motivation to keep tapping into this process again and again until it feels natural and non-negotiable.

I'm cheering for you!

Laura Buckley has a vision of a world in which people can live freely, fully, and authentically in the body they were born into. She is here to help you move away from prescribed norms and ideals around health and move toward a definition of wellbeing that feels true and attainable for you. Laura teaches a philosophy she calls "Body Partnership" to help you learn to treat the connection between mind, body, and spirit as the most important relationship in your life.

Laura is a registered dietitian and intuitive life coach who isn't afraid to step outside of traditional nutrition practices in order to help people achieve authentic wellbeing on their own terms because she believes that's how we create real results that actually light us up and that stand the test of time.

Laura draws on her education, experience, and intuition to help her clients unlearn old thought patterns and habits and create beliefs and behaviors that help them finally feel free and confident in their bodies. The way she seamlessly combines science and spirituality helps people feel deeply connected to themselves and their wellbeing.

Laura holds a BS in Nutrition Management from RIT, an MS in Adult Education from Buffalo State College, and a certificate in Organizational Consulting and Change Leadership from Georgetown University. She served for eight years in the US Army Medical Specialist Corps and then spent six years in organizational and interpersonal training and consulting before opening her coaching practice in 2017.

Book link: https://www.laurabuckleycoaching.com/ug-resource-page/

CHAPTER 9

ANIMAL WISDOM

A DEEPER CONNECTION TO YOUR SOUL

BY KIMBERLY FISHER, AEHP, RMT

MY STORY

It's 6:30 pm on a wet, dreary Wisconsin day. Walking into the kitchen, I place my wine bag on the floor, feeling frazzled after putting in an 80-hour workweek. Rounding the corner out of the kitchen into the living room of my bungalow home, I find Cote du Beaune lying on her bed. "Come on, let's go outside." Running out to get the mail, I come back in and notice she is not responding, not moving.

Alarmed, I drop to my knees and nudge her. Her eyes are droopy. Her body is lifeless. "Bonzy," my nickname for her, "Mama's home. Let's go outside." The love of my life, my teacher, my precious, 10-year-old yellow lab lays there unable to move. I bury my face into her fur, embracing her, and start to cry.

Bonzy, a rescue dog, came into my life when I was drowning in my job as a Sommelier, running the fine wine division for a large distributor. I named her Cotes du Beaune after a well-known wine region in France. I couldn't decide what to name her, so I gave her a name that represents my favorite growing region in France. She came to me with many physical and mental conditions, including bad hips, stomach sensitivities, fear of loud noises, and worst of all, fear of people. I worked with multiple veterinarians and integrated natural ways of healing to keep her comfortable, and eventually got her to trust again.

"Come on, hun, let's go outside," I urge her. With my help getting her off her bed, Bonzy stumbles to the back door. *Enough!* I pick up her fragile 50 pounds of trembling skin and bones and carry her to the car. She hadn't eaten in three days, and I knew it was time to get her help.

At the veterinary emergency hospital, we are escorted into a bright white waiting room with cold air blasting down on top of us. With nowhere to sit but a hard bench, Bonzy stands shivering with her tail tucked between her legs. Not wanting her to see my fear, I sit down on the cold linoleum floor and lay her between my legs. I place my silver puffy jacket over her shaking body. I stroke her soft fur and assure her everything is going to be okay. In the silence of the room, I hear, *I'm tired, Mom. I don't want to go on.*

"No! You can't leave; I'm not ready yet to be without you," I blurt out to no one.

Seven days prior, I laid curled up in a ball on my unyielding wood floor in the sunroom of my home, trembling, unable to move. Earlier in the morning, I noticed $5 left in my bank accounts. I lost my life's savings and lost my identity. In the following days after, with tears streaming down my cheeks and no reason to eat, I just laid there thinking about my future. I had no energy to move. I felt stripped of all my flesh, exposed, and left for bones.

On the floor, Bonzy places her fuzzy paw across my leg. I run my hands across her back and use all my healing tools to comfort her. *If I lose you, I will have officially lost everything!* I lean on top of her, crying in her soft ear, "Bonzy, you are my lab-adorable. You got this."

Finally, the doctor comes in and takes her back for an examination. Using all of her strength, I help her to her feet. She stumbles, struggling to walk, back legs dragging. Hours pass. When the doctor emerges from the back room, I ask, "Where is Bonzy?" "She's very dehydrated and underweight. We would like to keep her for additional testing and monitor her overnight."

"Can I see her?" I ask. Taking me to the back of the hospital, I see her in a kennel next to other dogs being kept for observation. I crawl in with her and squeeze her trembling body tight next to mine. "I'll be back tomorrow.

We'll have answers, and we will get you feeling better. I promise." I kiss her sweet wet nose and head for home.

Three days later, I'm called back to the same frigid waiting room to meet with the doctor. "Tests reveal there has been a lot of nerve damage. It's so severe that it has impacted Bonzy's mobility, and she may not be able to walk again. Her blood work suggests she has a rare tick disease found only in Michigan and upper Wisconsin. It might be time to be thinking of saying goodbye," the doctor spouts out.

Tears begin to pool in my eyes, and my ears fill with white noise. I stare at the animal anatomy posters on the walls. In my mind's eye, the room begins to fill with animals. All shapes, all sizes. *Am I on the boat with Noah and about to set sail?*

I drift off thinking about my experience being surrounded by the animals in 2008, nine years earlier. I feel a sharp blazing pain on my right side, the same pain I experienced back then. Originally misdiagnosed with appendicitis, I later went on to have two surgeries removing cancerous tumors from my liver. Through the help of an Ayurvedic Energy Healer, I learned more about my body and looked deeper into what western medicine was having a hard time identifying. I used natural ways of healing to get better. I used natural ways to help Bonzy in the past. Why now, am I hopeless, not able to do anything?

I continue thinking about lying in my bed in the recovery room from my first surgery. I dreamed I was walking in a vast wheat field, the sun glistening on the blades blowing in the wind, and hear a soft whisper in my ear. Next to me in the field, I see an elephant and a razorback gorilla. Thinking I was still under anesthesia, eyes glazed, I woke up and saw the images of the animals looking down on me. I realized later; this was the beginning of my connection with the animal allies.

I'm brought back to real-time hearing the door open and see a petite-sized woman carrying a clipboard. Letting the door close behind her, she takes a seat on the hard bench and starts to open the folders from the clipboard. "I'm one of the counselors here at the hospital and would like to discuss options and payment terms for services." Her approach to me was hard, like the bench she was sitting on. *What? How am I going to pay for this? And what other options are there? I have experienced the loss of my wealth, health, and now I could lose the love of my life.* I blurt out, "I would like to see her." Back in her kennel again, I wrap Bonzy in her favorite gray, fuzzy blanket I brought along with me. I kneel down on the floor, noticing her closed eyes and listless demeanor. I snuggle Bonzy next to my chest, lips pressed to her head, tears in my eyes.

For almost a decade, I used Ayurvedic medicine and energy work to heal myself, to heal others, and had used it to heal her. *Why can't I help her now?* Her heartbeat is racing next to my chest, and I say *Yes!* I knew I needed to find a way to change my negative energetics into a positive force that could propel her through this trauma.

I wrap her tighter, tears rolling down my face, whispering, "I will honor any decision you wish to make. Know I am here. The angels and animal guides are here to support and love you through this decision."

On the fourth morning of Bonzy's hospital stay, my phone rings. It's 6:30 am. "I'm calling with some news about Bonzy." "Yes," I clear my voice. "Bonzy has made considerable progress. She is eating, able to get up, and her bodily functions are working. You can pick her up today."

When I open my door to go to the hospital, I hear the caw of the black crows on the telephone wire. I look up and smile. I know from my training and experience working with animal totems that crows are a symbol of change and transformation. I couldn't wait to bring her home to help her heal and heal parts of me.

THE WAY FORWARD

From the day I brought Bonzy home from the hospital, our connection grew even stronger. I noticed things about Bonzy, and things about myself I neglected or didn't want to acknowledge during the stressful years of my career. I was able to hear her more clearly, and begin to understand both of our worlds better. She was mirroring my experiences throughout my life, and now I stared at her feeling her hopelessness. They say animals are the reflections of their owners, and this was a textbook version of it. She was a reflection of me.

Throughout these experiences, I fully understood grace and compassion are present in all animal life around us. Animals are a mirror into our souls. We are all connected. Every creature bears its spiritual gifts, and animals afford us visions of how our lives could be if we lived with a purity of thoughts and emotions.

Whatever happens, our way forward demands a sense of connecting. Treat every animal with love and compassion. Give gratitude for your connections with the animals and watch what unravels for you.

Bonzy went on to be my master teacher for one more year before her passing. She was able to get most of her mobility back and live comfortably. At the time of her passing, she was greeted by my grandma and many of the animal kingdom. From time to time, I hear the jingles of her collar, or she shows up during my sessions with clients. I'm forever grateful for the lessons taught and the connection we continue to share.

THE TOOL

HOW TO CONNECT WITH ANIMALS

AWARENESS

Pay attention to the nuances and moods of our two-legged, four-legged, finned, furred, and feathered friends around us. Be more sensitive to small changes.

CONNECTION

Helps you to see. It may not be what we want, but know it is part of the journey.

PAUSE

Causes us to shift our brain chemistry so we can consciously communicate with full acceptance, trust, and compassion. This transformational exercise is a heart to heart meditation, allowing you to connect more deeply from your heart to an animal's heart. Meditation can help us realize all the gifts the animals have given to us over time and see what else they can teach us about us. Our deeper knowing may be shown.

You can invite the animal in by relaxing your mind and body and meditating. Animals can enjoy the relaxation from a distance, but if they choose to come forward, allow them in.

AWARENESS EXERCISE

- Sit comfortably, place your feet on the ground with palms facing up towards the sky.
- Visualize your toes, heels, and feet permeating into the earth. Visualize your feet sinking through the dirt, making their way down through the rocks, and passing through the sand. Allow the coolness of the earth beneath you to encapsulate your entire feet.
- Now that you are deep into the earth imagine roots coming from your feet, going deeper, anchoring you into the cool waters in the center of the earth.
- With feet anchored in, visualize the color red, the earth's energy, traveling up your center, the Haro line, making its way through each of your Chakras: Root, Sacral, Solar Plexus, Heart, Throat, Third Eye, and Crown.
- Take a slow breath and allow the energy to settle.
- Next, from the Crown Chakra, visualize the color white, a connection to the divine. Breathe through each of the chakras allowing the energy to flow gently backward. Allow the color of white to travel from the Crown, Third Eye, Throat, Solar Plexus, Sacral and Root. Extend the white light, laser beaming it into the center of the earth.
- Connect the two colors of white and red together at the center of the earth. When you feel the connection, breathe gently, and let the colors flow through you like water; smooth, gentle, and easy.
- Now turn your focus to your heart. Place one hand on the high heart and the other hand on the lower heart.
- Visualize the two colors of red and white at the center point of the heart, molding into the color of pink. Swirl the pink energy color in a clockwise position to the high heart, low heart, front of the heart, and back of the heart. Feel yourself radiate love in and around you in all directions.
- Breathe slowly in through your nose for the count of three and release out through the mouth for the count of three. Repeat the breath three times. Feel the loving color of pink continue to radiate out

through each breath. Allow the energy to settle. As you radiate love and gratitude, take notice of feeling relaxed and expansive in your mind. Feel completely calm, centered, and balanced. Imagine your heart creating a beautiful state of trust, love, and compassion.

Allow this meditation to bring compassion to your life and invite the truths that may show up.

CONNECT EXERCISE

- Gather a picture of an animal. You may use a picture of a pet, a wild animal, or one from your memory.
- Begin to take a gentle gaze at the picture and make sure your physical movement, posture, and gaze are gentle and non-dominant. Allow yourself to be open to giving and receiving.
- Relax your lips. Breathe slowly and deeply and when you feel you have made a connection, ask permission to spend time with the animal. If the animal you are trying to connect with is not your own, introduce yourself to them. "Hi, my name is (Kimberly), and I would like to connect." In this connected space, obtaining messages may come by sensing things, seeing impressions, or hearing whispers. When experiencing any of these, thank the animal for sharing (focus on gratitude) and let the impressions float away, expressing positivity and openness, allowing more to be shown.

PAUSE EXERCISE

Take time to write down what you experienced with no judgments. Continue to have gratitude for what was shared. When your time has drawn to the end, thank your animal(s) for the information shared and ask if you may visit again.

THEIR WISDOM CAN BE OUR TEACHERS.

"Let Your Spirit Shine from the Inside Out" is the mantra of Kimberly Fisher, founder of Earthly Insights. After 25 years in corporate wine sales, Kimberly knew she was being nudged by the universe to explore deeper into the fiber of her being. She is a modern-day healer who blends the healing arts of Ayurveda, Reiki, and Shamanic practices to restore energy and spirit to both animals and humans. She is an Ayurvedic Energy Healing Practitioner (AEHP), Reiki Master Teacher of Usui and Tibetan (RMT), Reiki Master (RM) for animals, Medicinal Aromatherapist, and Certified Instructor of the Munay-Ki-Rites. She learned to heal animals through her interaction with her adopted rescue dog, Cote du Beaune, nicknamed Bonzy for short. Their journey together brought Kimberly's innate skills and passion to light as an Energy Healer for both people and animals.

Kimberly's compassionate style and magnetic energy help move clients to personal discovery. Whether you are in a private session, group class, or creative retreat, she shares messages from the animals who enter as teachers to offer guidance and support. Together she will tap into the magic of the natural world and help you create a life that is playful and authentic.

Kimberly has a comforting and supportive approach to letting the animal lead during an animal healing session and allows them to receive what is needed at the time. She has a nurturing spirit and honors the animal's unique mind, body, and spirit.

Kimberly is a dedicated student of life. She's an avid hiker, nature and outdoor enthusiast, adventure seeker, life explorer, and also can be found in the kitchen creating new dishes to share with friends and family.

She also offers "Connect to the Land" retreats, where Kimberly uses the wisdom of the elders of the plant and animal kingdom to help teach deeper ways to connect you to your true nature, radiating it out into the world.

To connect with Kimberly, explore one of her retreats, or sign up for her newsletter, visit:

Instagram: https://instagram.com/earthlyinsights

Facebook: @earthly.insights

Website: Earthlyinsights.com

Email: earthlyinsights@gmail.com

To listen to the audio version of the meditation, go to her resource page: https://www.earthlyinsights.com/resource

GIVING BACK

Kimberly's deep connection to Mother Earth and the animal allies inspires her to give back to non-profit organizations. Two recipients include: Big Dogs Huge Paws, whose philosophy is every big dog deserves a chance, with Bugatti Biscuits, and through her "Trust the Magic of your Heart" t-shirts, where she donates a portion of the sales to Glacier National Park Conservancy.

CHAPTER 10

UNDOING MEANINGS

THERE'S ALWAYS ANOTHER WAY OF SEEING

DOROTHY LENORE LLARIZA-TOME, B.A., M.ED.

MY STORY

Marriage and motherhood confused me greatly.

My parents openly admired each other, but I never saw them kiss, hug, nor cuddle intimately; neither did I hear them say 'I love you' in front of me. My grandparents appreciated each other in my presence and kissed, teased, and tickled each other. But Grandma also verbally bashed Grandpa to tears. When I got married to my first husband, I received lots of 'I love yous' and kisses and hugs, but I returned them doubtfully. My in-laws were genuinely loving and playful and sang accolades of each other, but they often and openly quarreled. By the time I was 18 years married with four children, I'd smashed countless plates against the garden wall, threatened to kill myself twice, and sought counseling from pastors, psychiatrists, and professors.

And there's Mother. The mothers in my immediate and extended families each had their unique mothering styles. Some used the word 'love' generously; some hardly ever mentioned it. One set up trust funds and bought expensive toys for her children while a few pinched and shamed their kids. Some embraced their kids in public and attended every school event, while a couple never celebrated birthdays. I was erratic. I sang lullabies, read stories, attended PTA meetings and recitals, but I also spanked and yanked, yelled and raged. I was on the verge of completely messing up childhood for my first two daughters when Montessori and Waldorf philosophies stepped in. My undoing had begun. Marriage and motherhood were to become my classrooms.

After the annulment of my first marriage in the Philippines (yes, that came undone), I moved to the US to marry my current beloved, John. I met John through my cousin, who served in the US Army. They both returned from deployment in Iraq when they vacationed in the Philippines. That meeting, and the falling in love that followed, was a melting away of a stubborn resolve. In my teen years, I swore that I would never patronize foreign products, never go to America, and never ever marry a foreigner. *Whoa!*

I knew I was entering new horizons with this major move to the US, but I was still shocked with what followed in the first five years or so; the dismantling of my long-held beliefs about almost everything, from concrete things to abstract notions. During the said years, for example, I clung to my prescriptions that sex with my American husband should be wildly exciting yet soulfully gentle, alternately scheduled and spontaneous, vibrant and varied, and that he should intuitively know when all these are supposed to happen! I had my interpretations each time his brows lifted, when he said, "uh-oh," and when he was silent.

My motherhood took a different turn too. It was challenged not only culturally and geographically but also developmentally. In this move, I brought my two younger children with me, both below 18 years old. Now I was observing, evaluating, and judging their words, body language, and facial expressions and measuring them against their new stepfather's words, body language, and facial expressions. I also felt guilty leaving behind my two older daughters.

I had a million interpretations of anything and everything. I intermittently felt happy one moment, then confused the next. Some days I was vibrant, other days humiliated; sometimes uplifted and confident, sometimes depressed and angry. I was exhausted. My children and husband were exhausted. This resulted in me questioning my self-worth, and guess what else? Marriage and motherhood! *What was going on with me?*

I only wanted peace and happiness. Thankfully, A Course in Miracles (commonly known as ACIM or the Course) accompanied John and me throughout my processes, which accounted for my positive moments. I studied the Course for over 15 years, but it was only during one group study with my new Vegas community that I became acutely aware of "an awareness" waiting to emerge.

"Dot," said Lisa, our teacher, "you're upset because you have a story of who you think you are. You're also running on a story of what you think being a wife is. And you have more stories of what you think being a mother is."

A story? A story of what I'm thinking!

Soon after John and I heard this usage of the word "story" for the first time, I confronted him about his work. "You're more focused on your work and education than on life itself." He replied simply with, "That's your story." I was dumbfounded. He did not contradict my statement nor validate it. He merely stated a fact. And no argument followed. His continued use of "that's your story" in my future confrontational moments untangled a lot of my messy stories.

What Lisa said made sense! A story is the meaning I give anything. And I was giving meaning from my unhealed, fearful mind, according to the Course! *Aha!* An unhealed mind? That's worth another chapter.

This new awareness immediately offered me three things:

1. There are ways of seeing new meanings about anything that upsets me.
2. My attachment to my story closes the door to other ways of seeing.
3. I am invited to release my attachment to any story that blocks my goal of peace.

This understanding changed my life, and I created my own tool based on the Course to share with others. It includes eight powerful statements to help you start your journey.

THE TOOL

UNDOING MEANINGS

"Undoing Meanings" is inspired by the word "undoing" from the Introduction to the Workbook for Students of A Course in Miracles (p. 929-930 Circle of Atonement @ 2017, emphasis by yours truly):

> "The purpose of the workbook is to train the mind in a systematic way to a different perception of everything in the world. The Workbook is divided into two sections, the first dealing with the ***undoing*** of the way you see now, and the second with the restoration of sight."
>
> "Some of the ideas you will find difficult to believe, and others will seem quite startling. It does not matter. You are merely asked to apply them as you are directed to do. You are not asked to judge them or even to believe them. You are merely asked to use them. Remember only this: You need not believe the ideas, you need not accept them, you need not welcome them. Some of them you may actively resist. None of this will matter or decrease their efficacy. But allow yourself to make no exceptions in applying the ideas the exercises contain. Whatever your reaction to the ideas may be, use them. Nothing more than this is required."

A little background on the Course: In the summer of 1965, Columbia University psychologist Helen Schucman and her boss, Bill Thetford, had reached a tipping point in their constant bickering with each other and the way most everyone in their department was back-stabbing each other. "There must be another way," Bill said in an attempt to cooperate, rather than compete. Helen, a 'militant atheist,' surprised him by agreeing. After that, she started receiving messages from a Voice that identified itself as belonging to Jesus. "This is a course in miracles," the Voice said. "Please take notes." For the next seven years, Helen channeled the Voice's dictation into what is now a spiritual classic, A Course in Miracles. Bill facilitated the typing of her shorthand notes. Although the Course uses Christian terminology such as "God, the Holy Spirit, miracles, atonement, and forgiveness," it is not religious in nature. It is a path of spiritual development in the form of an educational curriculum. The book contains the Text, Workbook for Students (one lesson a day for 365 days), and Manual for Teachers. It has undergone quite a few published editions to include shorthand notes from earliest manuscripts, cameo essays, and typographical corrections. (Please see References at the end of this chapter to access the book's different publications.)

My tool for healing, Undoing Meanings, is a set of eight statements (called Lessons) from the first section of the Workbook. Out of 365 Lessons, these eight stand out in their audacity to question all my perceptions and pre-conceived notions.

Here are the first four for the relinquishment of control and attachment over a way of seeing. These are exercises to undo the meaning of any perceived idea.

1. Nothing I see means anything.
2. I have given everything all the meaning it has for me.
3. I do not understand anything I see.
4. These thoughts do not mean anything.

Here are the next four as preliminary invitations to replace those that have been undone. These are about the willingness to trust the unknown.

5. Above all else, I want to see things differently.
6. There is another way of looking at the world.
7. I could see peace instead of this.
8. God is in everything I see because God is in my mind.

These are best posted for beginners where they can be easily accessed; on the phone, on a sheet of paper on the fridge, or in a journal. You can download a printable version from https://dottome.wordpress.com/services/#jp-carousel-248.

These are to be partnered with conscious exhalations and inhalations and silent pauses. "A comfortable sense of leisure is essential, not ritualistic," says the Workbook.

THE PROCESS AND THE EXAMPLE

As soon as something comes up for you that feels a little off, find a quiet spot in your environment, and pause. Be aware of the thought or the emotion that is surfacing. Perhaps it is upsetting or unsettling. Name it or describe it.

My argument with my daughter, who is experiencing depression, is causing me to fear that she will kill herself after this video call.

Acknowledge its presence. Look at it and feel it.

I feel afraid, upset, and angry. I am witnessing these feelings. I am feeling all these.

Exhale aloud and slowly through the mouth.

Haaaah... It is important to first exhale these heavy feelings.

Inhale deeply through the nose. Breathe normally.

Then subject the situation to these sentences:

1. *Nothing I see (about this argument) means anything.*
2. *I have given this (argument, this fearful threat) all the meaning it has for me.*
3. *I do not understand anything I see (about this whole thing).*
4. *These thoughts (about my daughter, about our argument, about my fear, about the call) do not mean anything.*

Pause. Witness the departing thought. Witness the departing feeling.

Exhale it aloud and slowly through the mouth.

Haaaah... When letting something go, it is important to exhale first.

Inhale deeply through the nose.

Breathe normally and continue with:

5. *Above all else, I want to see things differently. (Could there be another point of view?)*
6. *There is another way of looking at this. (I can be mistaken in my perception.)*

7. *I could see peace instead of this. (Maybe a less suspicious interpretation could lead to peace.)*

Inhale deeply through the nose. Now you are inhaling the desire for peace.

Exhale slowly through the mouth.

Breathe normally.

Wait for the next emerging thought. Witness it. If there's none, it's okay.

Then subject it to this sentence:

8. *God is in everything I see because God is in my mind. (My mind is not my brain. It is my connection with the Mind of God. I am not alone in seeing.)*

Inhale deeply through the nose. Now you are inhaling a new possibility.

Exhale slowly through the mouth. Perhaps nothing is presenting itself. Just witness the emerging peace.

Rest comfortably. Remember that this is not a ritual.

***

ANOTHER APPLICATION AND EXAMPLE

Since attachment to meanings is a block to peace, the Undoing must also be applied to dangerously juicy and pleasurable thoughts, experiences, and sensations that seem to linger far too long or deep. There is nothing wrong with pleasure and happiness per se; what needs to be undone is the meaning we assign to them and their sources, resulting to our attachment.

Be aware of such a thought.

My Facebook post is getting a lot of likes; I'm beginning to be popular. I love it!

Acknowledge the feelings that go with the thought.

I feel elated, giddy with pleasure and excitement. I want to replicate this feeling tomorrow. I want these feelings to stay.

Exhale aloud and slowly through the mouth.

Haaaah... It is important to first exhale when releasing something.

Inhale deeply through the nose. Breathe normally.

Then subject the situation to these sentences without being ritualistic:

1. *Nothing I see (about my Facebook post) means anything.*
2. *I have given this (number of likes, this feeling of popularity) all the meaning it has for me.*
3. *I do not understand anything I see (about the likes to the post).*
4. *These thoughts (about the pleasure and excitement, about wanting to hold on to the giddiness) do not mean anything.*

Pause. Witness the departing thought. Witness the departing feeling.

Exhale it aloud and slowly through the mouth.

Haaaah...

Inhale deeply through the nose.

Breathe normally and continue with:

5. *Above all else, I want to see things differently. (I don't want my feelings to be dependent on the number of likes.)*
6. *There is another way of looking at this. (I can be mistaken in my expectations.)*
7. *I could see peace instead of this. (I don't want to get addicted to this feeling of elation over people's reactions.)*

Inhale deeply through the nose. Now you are inhaling the desire for peace.

Exhale slowly through the mouth.

Breathe normally.

Wait for the next emerging thought. Witness it. Again, if there's none, it's okay.

Then subject it to this sentence:

8. *God is in everything I see because God is in my mind. (My mind is now turned over to the Mind of God for clearer and cleaner seeing.)*

Inhale deeply through the nose.

Exhale slowly through the mouth. Perhaps nothing is presenting itself. Just witness the emerging peace.

Rest comfortably.

***

A VARIATION

For students of the Course, there is a shorter version. Simply take an idea that you are ready to release and set it against these statements while breathing mindfully:

I am angry at COVID-19 for killing my friend last week.

Exhale aloud and slowly through the mouth.

Haaaah...

Inhale deeply through the nose. Breathe normally.

I have given this virus all the meaning it has for me. I have given this death all the meaning it has for me.

I have given this anger all the meaning it has for me. These thoughts about the virus, my friend's death, and my anger do not mean anything.

Pause. Witness the thoughts and feelings that come and go.

Exhale it aloud and slowly through the mouth. *Haaaah...*

Inhale deeply through the nose.

There is another way of looking at all of these. There is a bigger mystery. I don't know the whole thing, and it's okay.

Inhale deeply through the nose. Exhale slowly through the mouth.

Breathe normally. Wait for the next emerging thought. Witness it. Again, if there's none, it's okay.

God is in everything I see because God is in my mind. My right mind is in God's All-Knowing Mind.

Inhale deeply through the nose. Exhale slowly through the mouth.

Perhaps nothing is presenting itself. Just witness the emerging peace.

Rest comfortably.

***

You have just given up some old and calcified meanings you've been carrying around about a word or a situation. Now you're open to newer ways of seeing.

But while this is initially wonderful and refreshing, your mind could also be a vacant space unwittingly waiting to be occupied by other fear-based perceptions. *Oh, no!* You do not want this. What you want is your goal of peace. Over a hundred more lessons or statements are being offered by A Course in Miracles to occupy your vacant space and re-do your meanings. A printable version can be found at https://dottome.wordpress.com/services/#jp-carousel-249. Here are a few:

- My mind is part of God's. I am very holy.
- My holiness envelops everything I see.
- Love created me like itself.
- I am entitled to miracles.
- Today I will judge nothing that occurs.
- God, being love, is also happiness.
- Truth will correct all errors in my mind.
- There is no cruelty in God and none in me.
- I am not a body. I am free.
- I am in danger nowhere in the world.

***

The Course says that "words are symbols of symbols. They are thus twice removed from reality. The Teacher of God must learn to use words in a new way." So while the states of marriage and motherhood became my classrooms for undoing meanings, they, as words, also became my lessons on storytelling. My stories are no longer breeding grounds for fossilized attachments and addictions; they are open-ended and subject to undoing any time they sound tight and rigid. I am now more fluid and evolving than ever in my definitions, perceptions, and applications of words, and more allowing and inclusive of other people's meanings of words. And, of course, marriage and motherhood no longer confuse me.

May your Undoing of Meanings lead you to your goal of peace.

REFERENCE AND LINKS

Perry, R., (editor), (2017). A Course in Miracles. Based on the original handwritten notes of Helen Schucman (scribe). Complete & Annotated Edition. The Circle of Atonement, Inc., West Sedona, USA.

A Course in Miracles: https://circleofa.org/, https://www.jcim.net/acim_us/Acim.php, https://acim.org/

Dorothy "Dot" Lenore Llariza-Tome is a facilitator of A Course in Miracles in-person and online study groups, co-producer and co-host of the online show "On the Dot" at PHLV Radio (PH for Philippines and LV for Las Vegas), Certified Life Coach, and Certified Angel Card Reader. Her studies, experiences, and persistent interest in The Enneagram, the Law of Attraction, Montessori and Waldorf pedagogies, and non-duality thought systems are her guideposts in coaching family, friends, and clients in the US and the Philippines.

Dot is a Filipina living in Las Vegas, Nevada, USA, with her veteran husband, business-oriented son, and Siberian Husky. Her two eldest daughters are choreographers and writers based in the Philippines, while her third musician daughter is enjoying motherhood with her Austrian husband in Vienna. Dot longs to hug and kiss her grandson very soon. Dot holds a bachelor's degree in Humanities, major in Comparative Literature and Broadcast Communication and master's degree in Education, major in Teaching English as Secondary Language from the University of the Philippines.

Website: Love and Miracles – By Dot Tome (wordpress.com)

Blog: http://dotislove.blogspot.com/

Facebook personal: https://www.facebook.com/dorothylenore.llarizatome

Facebook community: https://www.facebook.com/loveandmiraclesbydot

LinkedIn: https://www.linkedin.com/in/dorothy-lenore-llariza-tome-5199424b/

Podcasts: https://www.iheart.com/podcast/966-phlv-radio-28926050

CHAPTER 11

SACRED SLEEP

CULTIVATE THE BEST SLEEP OF YOUR LIFE

KELLY MYERSON, MA, OTR

MY STORY

Darkness began to fall. My chest tightened, my palms began to sweat, and I felt panic rising. Breathing shallowly, I mentally ran through my list. *Bath, snuggles, song, sleep, place into crib.*

Most nights, our bedtime ritual allowed for a smooth transition to sleep, but not always. Sometimes, just as I was drifting to sleep, my son's cries would reach me through the monitor. My eyes glued to the blue screen, I'd plead, *please fall back to sleep, please fall back to sleep.*

When his cries didn't stop after a few minutes, I padded down the hallway, willing my body and mind to stay in the haze of sleep. Cuddling him close, he always fell asleep in my arms. He slept best curled up, head resting on my chest.

I was often exhausted in the morning, but the light of day gave me hope. Sunshine spoke of possibility and peace. I loved to wake and play with my little one. Curating play spaces became a pastime. Little minds adore new creative spaces.

Meanwhile, during those early years of poor sleep, my bedroom reflected chaos. Clutter was strewn about my dresser. Empty glasses gathered in groups on my nightstand. Laundry lived all about. Oh my, I had many unfinished baskets of laundry. My stress as nighttime arrived was reflected in the disorder in my bedroom.

I survived those early years of interrupted sleep, as most moms do. We learn to ride the wave of fatigue, grabbing extra caffeine or a quick nap if we're lucky! We share our exhaustion with other moms and accept it as part of the package deal for becoming a mother.

Ironically, I'm a sensory trained occupational therapist. I have spent the greater part of the past two decades coaching families in improving their child's sleep. What happens when we improve a child's sleep? Everyone sleeps better.

When we're struggling with sleep, it helps to develop an understanding of how our brain waves work. Our deep restorative sleep requires delta brain waves. Just above delta is theta. During theta brain wave activity, we are experiencing sleepiness just prior to drifting off to sleep.

Alpha is one step up and is a quiet, alert state. We are often in alpha for reading or learning. Beta is an active alert brain wave state. When we exercise or engage in physical activities, we are typically in beta. The final brain wave state is high beta. This is where I want you to lean in and read slowly. High beta is the brain wave state of anxiety, defense, and stress. Please read that sentence again.

When we climb into bed in a state of high stress or high beta, we are far away from delta. Multiple factors impact our ability to fall and stay asleep throughout our day. We can begin to improve the quality of our sleep by addressing key elements of our daily habits and our environment. If you've struggled with sleep for a long time or sleep challenges are new for you, I'm here to help.

These days I'm no longer triggered into a state of stress by darkness. For one, my son typically sleeps through the night. Additionally, my nighttime routine has become a fundamental component of my self-care practice. I have created, and I cultivate a sacred bedroom space. I feel joy and peace in the evening. Gone is the clutter. Gone are the overstuffed drawers.

My space is peaceful, calm, and sparse. Each item has been purposely placed and cared for daily. I curate my bedroom just as I created play spaces for my son. My sleep environment affords me rest and restorative sleep. I began, as you will, by envisioning the space in which you would feel restful and comfortable to sleep.

THE TOOL

The quality of our sleep has a tremendous impact on our well-being and health. Sadly, many of the people with whom I work are experiencing poor sleep. For many, disrupted sleep is a result of high levels of stress. However, individuals often present with ineffective habits and, as I shared in my story, disorganized sleep environments.

I am going to walk you through, step by step, to cultivate your own sacred sleep space and highlight several habits to ensure you are sleepy and relaxed by nightfall! Let's begin with the end in mind.

STEP 1: ENVISION YOUR DREAM SLEEP SPACE

Close your eyes and recall the most beautiful and comfortable bedroom in which you have ever slept. Perhaps it was somewhere you vacationed or a dream home you've seen on TV. Grab a notebook and describe the space. Bring in all your senses.

What do you see? Are there predominant colors that feel calming to you? Is it dark? What kind of lighting does it have? Does it have window treatments that allow for blocking out light?

How does it feel? Is the space sparse? What kind of furniture does it have? What textures are used in the space for bedding, area rugs, or other furniture?

What do you hear? Is there a fireplace? Is it soundproof? Do you have music playing? If so, is the music instrumental, a soundscape, or something else?

What do you smell? Are there scented candles or calming essential oils? How do they make you feel?

After answering these questions in your journal, do some research on the internet or in magazines. Find pictures or images which speak to your design.

STEP 2: CLEANING AND CLEARING

Next up, you will deep clean and declutter your bedroom. You can choose your favorite method for purging. Don't have one? I used Marie Kondo's method for reducing the clutter in my bedroom.

It may take you a few sessions to clear, depending on the condition of your bedroom. I advise setting a timer for ten minutes and tackling one small area such as your nightstand or the top of your dresser. During those ten minutes, light a candle, play your favorite music, and even dance as you're cleaning! I have found pairing cleaning and decluttering with enjoyable activities and sensations reinforces how good it feels to get organized!

I began with my clothing. You can too! Place all your clothing on your bed and keep only the items you genuinely love. Be sure to complete this in one session. I've fallen into the trap of pulling something apart and not following through to completion. It never ends well. I feel disappointed in myself, and I've created more mess. Instead, push through to the end. Bring your bags to a donation site of your choice, or even schedule a pickup at your house.

Celebrate all your decluttering accomplishments. Treat yourself with a hot cup of tea, a piece of chocolate, or whatever small treat lights you up.

STEP 3: TENDING AND TIDYING

You have celebrated a clean and now decluttered bedroom space. Now you want to keep it free of clutter. I use a process of tending and tidying. These are two daily habits. You will tend to the space through regular cleaning. My tidying habit involves returning items in my bedroom to where they belong. For example, I bring empty water glasses to the dishwasher, used tissues go into the garbage, dirty socks into the hamper, jewelry goes in the jewelry box, receipts from my pockets get filed, and change goes into the piggy bank. I also commit to washing, drying, folding, and putting away each basket of laundry right away. I carry these tasks to completion.

Before you leave your bedroom, throughout the day, look around and ask yourself, "what can I tend to or tidy?" I find these two practices keep my bedroom from becoming chaotic. Additionally, keep your surfaces free of clutter. It feels so good to enter a clean and clutter-free bedroom.

STEP 4: MAKE YOUR BED

You can create an even more delightful space by making your bed every day. It doesn't have to be fancy unless you desire it to be. Simply draw up the covers and place the pillows neatly at the top of the bed. Fold any extra blankets.

Walking into my bedroom in the evening with the combination of a made bed and a clean space is wonderful. It's as if I have opened the door to a hotel room. Yes, I am the one cultivating and keeping the space, but it still feels serene.

After the first four steps, take a moment to celebrate! Appreciate your ability to accomplish a new special space for yourself. I'd like to note; I didn't spend any extra money when I first reset my bedroom. I used items I already had available to me. You don't need to buy new furniture or bedding. A clean and clear space is available to you now.

A final note. Aim for progress and not perfection. I'm speaking to my fellow perfectionists here! If you find the room returns to a former state of chaos, begin again. Each small step you take towards curating a sacred space is amazing. You are learning and changing your mindset as you go. Let's explore the new habits you'll be cultivating next.

STEP 5: REMOVE TECHNOLOGY FROM YOUR BEDROOM

For some of you, this is a big step. Spending time on your phone and tablet, watching TV, or using a computer in your bedroom could be disrupting your sleep. Your space should reinforce relaxation to encourage your brain to shift down to theta and then delta brainwaves. Watching TV or scrolling on your social media feed before bed stimulates your brain and may negatively impact your ability to fall asleep.

Are you someone who likes to read on your tablet or phone before bed? If so, adjust the settings on your device to reduce blue light and turn down the brightness. You can also decrease glare with night mode or dark mode.

One of the concerns I often hear from people is not having their cell phone nearby in case someone calls with an emergency. I recommend either plugging it in across the room or in an adjacent room. If your phone is not next to you, you're less likely to wake up and look at your phone in the middle of the night.

STEP 6: INVITE YOUR SENSES

You have successfully removed technology, so what will you bring into your room? Go back to what you wrote in your journal in Step 1. How can you incorporate some of those elements in your bedroom?

What would you like to see in the space? Can you add or change colors in your room that feel calming to you? Can you adjust the amount of light coming in or add a dimmer?

What would you like to feel in your new space? Can you add new textures through bedding, window treatments, or other furniture?

What would you like to hear? Would you like to add a sound machine for white noise or curtains to block outside sound? What music makes you feel calm?

What would you like to smell? Do you have a favorite scented candle or calming essential oils?

Can you create a space to sit and read or meditate?

STEP 7: MINDFUL PRACTICES

What do you feed your head all day? Nourishing our minds is as important as nourishing our bodies. I'm a proponent of the following daily practices. Feel free to add more to this list.

- Practice daily mirror affirmations.
- Write five items in a gratitude journal each evening.
- Read or listen to positive content such as books, podcasts, Audible books, etc.
- Limit exposure to violent or disturbing content on TV or in movies.
- Limit time on social media.
- Engage in prayer, meditation, or your preferred spiritual practices.

STEP 8: MIND DUMPING

This step is for my fellow busy brains. We get snuggled into bed and our minds, grateful for the silence, begin running through a litany of worries, to-do lists, and amazing ideas. I'm grateful for my mind, but I don't need to celebrate its capacity for thought as I'm trying to fall asleep.

I encourage you to get a notebook and a pen. Choose a comfy spot other than your bed. We're pairing a mind dump with a location other than your bed on purpose.

Sit with your pen and notebook 30 minutes before you go to bed. Close your eyes and take several deep breaths. Invite your mind to empty itself onto the page. Write down everything. Don't worry about organizing; get it all out onto the page. Write out your grocery list, to-do lists, things you're worried about, anything and everything which comes to mind. By recording these items, you reduce overthinking at bedtime.

You can play with how long you spend mind dumping. You may find some days you have more to write. This list can be used during a work planning session or even feed into some journaling. In the beginning, you may also want to leave the notebook next to your bed in case something pops up as you lay your head down on the pillow.

STEP 9: TECHNOLOGY FASTING

Technology fasting has become one of the most impactful practices I have built into my daily routine. I take a break from technology from around 8 pm until 7 am the next day. You will simply plug in your phone and walk away. This is a great time to mind dump or read a book. These quiet activities calm your body and your mind.

Initially, I took a daily technology break to improve my sleep. However, it has had some awesome side benefits. By putting away my phone at 8 pm, I am available for my son's bedtime routine and then my own. I begin my day tuned into myself with a beautiful morning routine. My mindful practices and joy-filled activities set the tone for my day.

STEP 10: BEDTIME COUNTDOWN

It's the final countdown! You've cultivated your dream bedroom space and incorporated new mindful habits. Now it's time to build the best routine to be ready to fall asleep.

8-12 hours before bed, stop consumption of caffeinated beverages. Caffeine can remain in your system for up to 12 hours after it was consumed. If you're aiming for a 9 pm bedtime, it may mean avoiding a delicious afternoon cup of coffee.

4 hours before bed, stop high impact exercise. Exercise is great for your body and can give you boundless energy. Use this to your advantage and exercise earlier in the day. Yoga or stretching before bed can be great for winding down at the end of the day.

2-3 hours before bed, stop the use of screens. This is the recommendation of the American Academy of Pediatrics for children and occupational therapists everywhere. Although children are most vulnerable to the light and waves of screens, adults are not immune to their impact on sleep.

Bedtime

Take a moment to savor the comfort of your clear and cultivated sleep space. Turn down your sheets, listen to soothing music, and enjoy a scented candle or essential oils. As you lay your head onto your pillow, drop into gratitude for your commitment to sacred sleep. Breathe deep and sink into your bed.

On the days you find your mind busy, here's a little trick. As you drift off to sleep, visualize each moment of the next day. Picture every minute in your mind's eye. Color your day with possibility and positivity. See every encounter and task turning out better than you can imagine.

I wish you deep, restorative sleep so you may get the best out of all your waking hours.

RESOURCES

Visit my resource link for recordings of the guiding questions for envisioning your dream space and more at https://beingwellwithkelly.com/ultimateguideresources.

Kelly Myerson is an author, speaker, and coach who will cultivate space for you to emerge from stress and overwhelm to lead and savor the life of your dreams! A sensory trained occupational therapist and holistic entrepreneur, she brings a wealth of experience and fun science to inspire her clients.

With a master's degree in Strategic Communication and Leadership, she has a unique skill set for creating lasting change. Kelly has two books in the works and speaks out for working moms emphasizing radical self-care. She believes the journey toward healing and wellness begins with one small step. Each small step builds on the next until you find yourself embodying wellness. Come join Kelly's community and connect with her at https://www.beingwellwithkelly.com.

CHAPTER 12

DITCH THE DYSFUNCTION

USING PERSONAL ASTROLOGY TO FIND YOUR TRUE POWER

BY KARIN M. YEARWOOD

MY STORY

My father is an adulterer. So was his father. And maybe even his father. My paternal family is generationally cursed. I have six siblings: one full-blooded brother, two half-sisters, and three half brothers. My father has one wife and two mistresses.

Infidelity is not the sole offense. My father's narcissistic personality disorder has led to a lifelong trauma bond between him and my mother (the wife). Trauma bonds occur when one or both persons in a relationship use a collection of manipulation tactics like brainwashing, guilt-tripping, and "perceived acts of kindness" to coax the other person into believing there is no abuse in the union.

I've accepted being the fallout of wedlock between an altruistic narcissistic father and severely codependent mother. Dysfunctional communication methods, abandonment, neglect, humiliation, disrespect, betrayal, poor boundaries; were all baked into my programming and ultimately led to my PTSD crash around age 30. The "crash" speaks to a sudden breakdown of internal structures installed early in life; the programming.

For mystics, occultists, lightworkers, spiritual teachers, and those drawn to metaphysics, there are many ways to describe the process of having a PTSD crash. One is the dark night of the soul (DNS). DNS is a stage of personal development where one undergoes a painful transition– often with depression, anxiety, flashbacks, insomnia, and mood swings—to a deeper sense of self.

Another way to describe a PTSD crash, and how I've come to explain this time in my life, is the Saturn return. This is an age-specific natal planetary transit in Western astrology. After we are born, the planet Saturn travels through all 12 zodiac signs, and it makes its way back to your natal placement of Saturn. Since it takes about 29 years for this transit to complete, the Saturn return is experienced between ages 28 and 31, but the energies can be felt beyond those ages.

For me, my Saturn return was more than simply exiting my twenties and entering my 30s. To be clear, everyone does not experience an intense Saturn return. This is where our soul's karma and dharma come into play. What we have incarnated into this life to do is unique, and we all have different timelines for what happens in our lives. Our ego controls what plays out in the physical plane (mundane, day-to-day), and our higher self controls what we manifest and attract. Our egos create karma; our higher selves take us through dharma.

For all of my life, I carried a deeply rooted sense of shame about my family dynamic. Each stage of my development from childhood to adulthood carried its own theme, and with each developmental stage, my role changed. Dysfunctional families are made up of members with assigned roles. Although sometimes, role assignment is given indirectly and is merely a result of the child's personality, it frames their programming in particular ways. As a young child, I had no cognitive understanding of how atypical my family is. After all, my father never displayed any shame or remorse for his adulterous ways. No one blatantly gave me my role, but hindsight is 20/20, and I see my past, child self as the lost child.

According to Gabrielle Applebury's *6 Dysfunctional Family Roles and Their Characteristics*:

> The lost child attempts to blend into the background as much as possible to keep themselves safe and to avoid rocking the (sinking)

boat. They may feel ignored, neglected, and scared to draw attention to themselves, especially in abusive households. The lost child:

- May be described as a loner.
- May have difficulty developing social skills and self-esteem.

As an adult, the lost child may struggle with friendships and romantic relationships. They may prefer to be alone, as this can feel tied to their emotional and/or physical safety.

There was an insidious norm to our family interactions. There were no secrets, yet the adults had very cunning communication styles. I think this gave way to my empathic nature and heightened intuition. I always had to read between the lines and piece together any and every given scenario.

Despite carrying the energy of a lost child, I wouldn't say my childhood was tumultuous. My father would take my brother and me to play with our half-siblings. The summers were really fun. I enjoyed going to amusement parks, carnivals, and festivals with all of us. I didn't even see them as "half-siblings." They were just the brothers and sisters that had different houses. Sometimes their mothers (the other women) would spend time with us too. It was like my father really had three different families. Interestingly, our childhood outings never included my mother—just the mothers of my half-siblings.

As a young adolescent, I shifted from innocently accepting the dishonest and immoral lifestyle that my parents lived and began having feelings of shame. My role didn't completely shift from lost child; instead, it compounded to also being the hero child. My hero position was restricted for my mother. Only she required this of me, but again hindsight offers a clearer perspective, and I now see that my mother projected this role onto me. In truth, she carried the energy of "hero." She chose to see our family as "not so bad" because there are worse things in other families. Her codependency was a blockage to saying no, releasing control, and being carefree. Upholding a family facade was the only way she knew to maintain a sense of self.

My extended family accepted this behavior and lifestyle and oddly seemed to be proud of it. Unpacking the collective family unit, specifically my paternal family, would require significant time and space, so I won't do that here.

What I've gleaned from this upbringing is that my soul's journey involves many karmic experiences, and as a result, my Saturn return was coupled with a dark night of the soul. My assigned roles were a part of my psychological programming. Consequently, I created stories that distorted my sense of self and my reality. We all are made of stories that allow our programming to run smoothly or to malfunction. When I realized my collection of stories did not align with my life path, that triggered an alchemical process of purging and renewal.

THE TOOL

Our subconscious programming drives about 80% of our behaviors and decisions. The aspect of this that many of us overlook is the metaphysical components that fuse with the psychological—things like natural law, mysticism, occultism, and psychic development. Familial karma is complex and often involves a collection of non-cohesive broken strands. At various points in life, we wrap these strands around a perceived area of importance. It could be a job, a person, a reputation, location, or anything conceivable to the rational mind.

That's kind of how personal astrology can work for you. It dislodges you from a self-imposed constrictive tunnel of vision toward your destiny. Of course, the day-to-day realities of the human experience like managing money, developing a career, building healthy relationships, and establishing a healthy sense of self can thwart the process of becoming fully empowered (Duriel 2020).

Let's instead look to the cosmos for our blueprint to intentional, balanced, and fulfilling lives.

Dysfunction shape-shifts. It takes form in the irregular happenings of the physical plane (3D). Things like a busy kitchen in a coffee shop that always runs out of sugar at 8 am, daily traffic jams that happen like clockwork, or sudden technical glitches. This dysfunction is here and now. In and out.

The dysfunction within our higher selves results from the distorted connection to higher planes. It can, however, manifest in the physical plane. We see this through our family relationships that are continuously in conflict. We see it in the toxic cycles in romantic partnerships and one-sided friendships. I don't think I've ever been connected to myself. Familial dysfunction has a way of detaching your subtle body from the physical body. The subtle body vibrates at a higher frequency than our physical body, though both are interconnected (*The Little Work*, Duriel 2020).

Psychological trauma scatters your energy into fragments. When you give your power away, you lose little pieces of yourself—saying yes when your soul screams no. Your sense of self becomes so fractured that even the most obvious direction couldn't lead you to total fulfillment. But that's the thing. How do we know what leads us to our destiny? Perhaps there isn't a definite answer. But we can most certainly embody the energies that will hold us in our highest esteem.

It has to do with the notion of as above, so below. Perhaps the most inspiring lesson from intentionally making a soul pivot is realizing just how powerful we are in guiding and shaping what comes to us. When we ditch the dysfunction, we create a clearer path to physical manifestation. We, in essence, "pull down" from the higher planes through what we focus on, our thoughts (both conscious and subconscious), words, emotions, and actions.

Soul purpose is prefaced with soul awareness. When we become self-aware, we can begin soul revival. Using our natal charts is one of many modalities that can reveal our soul's destiny. Many things can distort our connection to self and connection to Source. Whatever Source means to you, soul revival does not matter if you are not connected to self.

Personal astrology allows us to use energies from the cosmos as guideposts for all aspects of life: Love and intimacy, career and professional life, family dynamics, ancestral wounds, self-expression, and other time-sensitive events.

The natal chart is the snapshot of the sky at the very moment you were born.

Your personal astrology comprises all the planetary placements and positions in your natal chart. The natal chart is a sphere with 12 sections or houses, one for each zodiac sign accompanied with a planet. A circle is

360 degrees, so each section or house is 30 degrees. Each house represents an aspect of our lives. The first house is the house of self-expression, the second house represents our material goods and the value we give them, the third house rules communication, and so on. Each sign is of one of the four elements; air, fire, water, earth. Every planet rules one of the signs, except Venus and Mercury, which each rule two signs. The natal chart can be considered a blueprint or a script for our human experience. You can study it, but we are all given free will, so the mere placements in the chart do not determine your fate.

The sun sign is a blanket energy for the natal chart. Our sun sign reflects the position of the sun on the day you were born. The sun sits in each zodiac sign for approximately 30 days. In Western astrology, the sun is considered a planet. It describes your personality at the core, your sense of self, and general preferences. Our sun sign backs every aspect of our life, but considering the natal chart as a whole, the sun sign is only a very small aspect of your overall disposition.

The ascendant (rising) sign is perhaps the most integral part of our natal charts. It is not a planet but a horizontal line that starts at the 9 o'clock mark and runs across the chart. It sets off the "house" placements. The zodiac sign that the ascendent line hits is your rising sign. It carries the energy of how you project yourself to others; it's how others perceive you. It is not necessarily how you feel about yourself. Understanding the characteristics of your rising sign can help you identify blind spots in your relationships. This is crucial if you've experienced trauma or neglect because you may be working in the shadow side of the rising sign; that is the sign's unconscious aspect.

For example, if you are a Gemini ascendant, you most likely are a great communicator, very social, creative, and open minded. But the shadow side of Gemini involves being too superficial, starting gossip or using formidable language, sharp mood swings, etc. Being raised in an emotionally dysfunctional family could definitely trigger the shadow aspects of this sign.

There are three pillars for finding your true power with personal astrology.

The moon sign is where the moon was placed at the time of your birth. The moon is also considered a planet in personal astrology. It tells how you govern your emotions, the ebb and flow of your moods, and any emotional attachments we developed in childhood. The zodiac sign of your moon placement indicates the energies of ancestral wounds you carry. What house the moon is placed in determines what area of your life is most affected by that ancestral wound. My moon is placed in the 4th house in the sign of Leo. The fourth house is the house of foundation, family, and stability. Leo is a fire sign and fiercely loyal. Because my moon is placed here, it indicates that my ancestral wound is linked to my family and sense of kinship. It also means that there is a dysfunction surrounding loyalty. Because of Leo's fire element, the dysfunction in my family is passionate, and I feel passionate about it. Hence I have shared this part of my life with you.

The Chiron is not a planet or sign but a comet that orbits the solar system. In astrology, our Chiron represents our soul wound. Your Chiron's sign and house placement indicates what the wound is and what area of your life it appears in strongly. It's the weakness that we need to heal most in our human experience, yet we do not possess the ability to do so on our own. It is through helping others heal this same wound, we, in turn, heal ourselves. The Chiron is the "wounded healer."

My Chiron is placed in the sign of Gemini in the second house, the house of personal finances and values. As you can imagine, I've struggled to know my value and how to properly discern the value others bring to my life. I've allowed poor treatment, dishonesty, and takers to extract my time, money, and energy. Gemini is an air sign and ruled by Mercury, so it's highly intelligent and communicative energy. However, a soul wound in Gemini means effective communication is a challenge. I struggle to communicate my value authentically.

Our true node or north node is the dharma we are meant to work through in the human experience. It describes how we need to work through karma to grow exponentially as magical beings. The north node is our peak ascension. The placement in our natal chart tells us the area of our life that our soul is meant to do the most work. It is perhaps also telling of the obstacles and challenges we will face to reach that ascension.

My north node is in the 12th house in the sign of Aries. My soul's destiny is rooted in pioneering esoteric services that will catapult mystic healers to divine leadership.

Astrology is incredibly vast. Even the most experienced and knowledgeable astrologers are still learning the infinite aspects of this pseudoscience. What I am explaining here is a very introductory, scratch the surface tenet of personal astrology.

Karin M. Yearwood is an intuitive guidance counselor who specializes in Life Path Astrology™ Readings, tarot readings, hypnosis, and esoteric healing instruction. Her mission is to guide divine leaders on their journey of self-healing, self-discovery, and visioning after adverse experiences. Karin has a gift of helping individuals evolve through their own spiritual awakening and transformation.

Using her 3-step Halfway to Whole Method, Karin works with kindred souls and change-makers to discover their purpose and their life's mission.

She also holds a master's degree in professional writing and works as an adjunct English professor.

To learn more about your personal astrology, visit https://www.karinmyearwood.com.

CHAPTER 13

ENERGY ALIGNMENT METHOD

FINDING YOUR TRUE CALLING IN LIFE

BY ESTHER APOUSSIDIS, MSC, BA (HONS), MFHT

MY (HEART) STORY

It was a dull, dreary Thursday afternoon in mid-November. Nothing out of the ordinary, except that my mother was languishing in hospital. Was it only ten days earlier than we were both soaking up the glorious Iberian sun, finding a little respite from the damp Welsh weather? It was a wonderful birthday treat from my eldest son to celebrate my 50th Birthday. And for my mother, it was a trip down memory lane, imbibing the panoramic vista of Ronda and the charms of Seville, where she once enjoyed the pleasurable company of my father not too long before his all too rapid demise from cancer.

It was difficult to believe things could appear so normal. I was cleaning and tidying up in our beautiful little coffee shop with its continental flourish, what one might call a delicate jewel in the heart of a rugged former mining community in South Wales.

But something quite distinct did happen that late afternoon. I was suddenly overcome with a most compelling, deep-seated longing and impulse to visit my mother in the hospital. I was there the previous Saturday and planned a second visit the subsequent Saturday (in two days). My heart seemed to implore me to go to the hospital: *go to your mother*. But my head gave me ample, logical reasons not to. My head reasoned that by the time I finished the cleaning, did a little shopping, prepared supper, fed my three boys (aged 5, 11, and 17 at the time), and traveled to the hospital, I would have only 15 minutes to spare. *That's a ridiculously short time to warrant a 25-minute car journey there and back.* So the head won, and I squashed the heart impulse.

But it was a bitter victory. When I arrived at the coffee shop the next morning, where my 17-year-old was already serving our first customers of the day, he greeted me all flustered, "Mom, Dom just dropped by and left you an urgent message. He said to get to the hospital as soon as you can; something bad has happened." My heart immediately lurched.

My mother experienced a stroke, but even then, I did not register the severity of the situation (always hoping for the best outcome). I dropped my shopping and gulped back the sobs. Customers could see my distress, and one of them rushed in consternation over to me, "Are you okay? Do you need a lift? Do you want me to get you anything?" I automatically said, "No, I'll be fine," but felt the blood drain from my face. I was beginning to feel disoriented and disconnected from my world.

The car journey seemed interminable, and the traffic lights were warring against me, an incessant, angry red streak, causing my stomach to churn and my heart to beat wildly in my chest. I felt like I was drowning in panic, and I could scarcely come up for air. At last, I arrived at my destination. I couldn't run fast enough to the information desk. "I'm desperate to know where my mother is. Her name is Helga Clarke. It's critical that I get to see her and find out how she is."

I just needed confirmation that my mother was where I left her the previous Saturday. I felt like I was wading through treacle or against a strong river current as I made my legs carry me to the ward. When I finally arrived, my mother was already drifting out of consciousness, but I like to think I managed to get the tiniest squeeze out of her hand after I announced, "I'm here, Mom, I'm here for you, please hang on." Gripping her hand, I thought I could pass on to her my own willpower, strength, and determination to overcome.

By the time the results came through from the brain scan, my brothers, my sister, and I had assembled in a private waiting room. We waited with bated breath as the doctor came in. With a grave countenance and a carefully modulated tone, she announced, "Your mother has experienced a severe stroke. Her body could no longer fight this latest virus. Her whole immune system has collapsed. She's been waging this war for too long, and it's taken its toll. It was inevitable, and just a matter of time." And so we learned that she would not survive the day. And sure enough, within a few hours, her body died, and her soul departed, leaving the whole family absolutely heart-stricken and bereft.

I will never forget that memory of remorse, pain, and anguish. I know now that my heart was receiving and passing on a message from my mother or God. She was calling out to me to allow me to bid her farewell. It was time for her to terminate her suffering and long battle with pain and rejoin her beloved husband.

And if I'm not mistaken, my heart spoke to me before with a powerful message. It was a year and a half before that fateful day in November, when we were about to sign the lease on a second coffee shop in Cardiff (South Wales). My head and hands crafted a beautiful business plan, backed up by research undertaken by my husband. Despite all the detailed analysis and financial projections, something didn't really connect to my heart. My gut impulse was to run a mile, but my husband had committed so much energy, passion, and interest to this venture. "Don't worry. You're overthinking this; I've done the research, everyone I've asked for feedback thinks it will be raging success."

I didn't have the "heart" to rebuff him and suggest that I thought this project too risky. With hindsight, I know this was another powerful heart lesson. We paid a steep price. After a mere six months of trading, we had to close the business. The money was gushing out faster than it was coming in. My husband was back in free-fall, sick with worry about his mother in Greece degenerating rapidly from Alzheimer's, and worried about losing everything, including his health and his sanity. We did almost lose the roof over our heads, and I actually did lose my entire life's savings; my pension was no more!

It hasn't been an easy path to trust my heart. I was so long conditioned by my upbringing, my parents, society, and the corporate world to act from the head. I learned to analyze, brainstorm, strategize, plan, control, and manipulate; to execute, implement, and accomplish; all measures relying on the head energy for inspiration, ingenuity, and guidance. But when we let the head dominate, there is no room for spirit, no room for divine guidance, no room for trusting in our co-creative source power, and no room to decipher our true purpose and Dharma. That's because the heart is disconnected. The heart is the bearer and messenger of our feelings and the conduit to our soul. After all, we are human BEINGS, not human DOINGS. And in doing what the head says all the time, we are negating our true essence, our quintessential being.

THE TOOL

THE ENERGY ALIGNMENT METHOD (EAM)

Not long after closing the doors on the two coffee shops, I embarked on a new transformational journey. I studied holistic therapies and, in doing so, stumbled upon the Energy Alignment Method created by Yvette Taylor. I was intrigued and fascinated by this process of using the body as a pendulum and biofeedback mechanism to determine what is going on with our energy, on all levels, in all forms, and at all times: past, present, and future. I marveled at the simplicity of asking the "sway" what is holding us back. I learned to ask about our fears, phobias, tensions, pre-occupations, limiting beliefs, emotional patterns, and anxieties. And I learned how to instruct ourselves to release them, no matter the origin, level, or intensity of resistance. It was such a simple, easy process. I was hooked! And we don't just release them for ourselves, from our past and present. We release them going forward for our offspring too. And because nature abhors a vacuum, we ensure that once resistant or very stagnant energy (what we call "reversed" energy in EAM) is released, we align to a higher vibration energy that is empowering and life-affirmative.

And thus began my three years of learning, implementing, and mentor training in the Energy Alignment Method (EAM). This training incorporated the study of Universal Laws, Eastern energy healing philosophies, and a familiarization of Western quantum physics and neuroscience. EAM is founded on the idea of neuroplasticity, that we can rewire our mind to think and believe differently and break old habits and patterns of beliefs and thoughts (even those more entrenched and passed on to us from generation to generation). Holding on to past negativity in whatever energetic form does not serve us, so we learn to relinquish and align to more positive emotions, beliefs, and thoughts that empower us to move forward in life.

EAM identifies three states of energy: in flow, in resistance, and in reversal.

ENERGY IN FLOW

When our energy is in flow, we are in high vibe energy, things appear effortless, and all is plain sailing. There are no (or seldom) doubts, anxieties, fears, or negative emotions. We are extremely positive on all fronts, and all is balanced and aligned. We are in tune with the Universe and our higher self. The conscious and subconscious minds are working in harmonious union. There is no energetic dissonance. What is important to note is that our subconscious mind (which EAM taps into) is over a million times more powerful than our conscious mind in controlling our state of flow. Being in flow not only affects our ability to manifest and our capacity to feel great and think expansive thoughts; it also means that physiologically the cells and cellular mechanisms of our bodies are in flow and working optimally for best health and longevity. It also signifies that our spiritual wellbeing is at its peak, and we are expressing ourselves more intuitively and psychically.

ENERGY IN RESISTANCE

When our energy is in resistance, it's as if we're taking one step forward and two steps back. We're pulled in two directions at once. There is some movement, but most of it is not going in the right direction. Resistance can be in any layer of the energy aura, often of a mental (belief) or emotional type. Resistance can express itself as patterns, including generational or past life ones. They can also be passed on in the womb. We're in resistance when we're susceptible to conflicting emotions or beliefs that lead to tension and inability to resolve an issue. Resistance emotionally or mentally releases stress hormones in the body and contracts energy flow in the cells so that over time we're more prone to illness and infection.

ENERGY IN REVERSAL

In this scenario, the energy is moving backward. This means the person is completely stuck and cannot move forward. It's akin to ground-hog day (déjà-vu with a negative spin). This phenomenon is often induced by trauma, a catastrophic event or major upheaval in this life, a previous generation, or in another past life. There is an impasse, and there is no way to effect change or move forward without first releasing the reversal. In this state, if prolonged, our cell functions start to shut down, and we become chronically ill.

The key to using EAM is to release reversals and resistances by determining how these show up in our energy (as an emotion, belief, or thought, behavioral pattern, or simply an abstract form of energetic resistance). We express these in a way that makes sense to us. Thus, it can be kinesthetically (how does it feel in the body? Is there heaviness or a constriction somewhere?), visually (what image, shape, or color comes to mind?), or numerically, i.e., number of resistances. Numbers help when connected to beliefs, analytical thinking, or if the resistance is abstract or beyond our conscious mind to fathom.

Following is an example of using the 5-step process of EAM to release a resistant belief around the notion of "I am not good enough." Please note we do this by standing with legs hip-width apart, knees unlocked, and arms loosely hanging down by our side. All questions are said out loud.

Step 1: "Do I have a resistant belief that I am not good enough?"

Step 2: The body lurches forward (usually a pull from the gut/solar plexus area) to indicate a yes and a backward sway to suggest a no. An indeterminate sway indicates a reversal, which must be released first (similar to releasing a resistance applying Steps 4 and 5).

Step 3: "How many resistances do I have around the belief that I am not good enough?" "Do I have more than 50?" "Do I have more than 100?" The sway will indicate yes/no to each question until we get the right number.

Step 4: We release/transform the resistance by stating, "I am ready to release all (e.g. 100) resistances around the belief that I am not good enough. I release these from my energy in all forms, on all levels and at all points in time." (Say three times as a minimum).

> Step 5: Manifest / align with a positive belief to counter the previous negative. For example: "I am ready to allow the belief or conviction that I am good enough. I welcome this with joy and empowerment into my energy in all forms, on all levels, at all points in time." (Say three times as a minimum). With Step 5, arms can be uplifted into a funnel shape to "welcome" in the positive belief or emotion.

We can apply this process to any resistant emotion, belief, or thought and align to something empowering and uplifting. The objective is to move from low vibration energy to high vibration energy (i.e., high-frequency emotions of love, joy, freedom, and empowerment). Why do this? Because by being in high vibration energy, we can activate through the quantum field the Law of Attraction. Like attracts like (both for good and for bad). Thus, when we vibrate in high, positive energy, we attract positive events, circumstances, and people into our lives. It is a manifesting energy, where we can manifest health, wealth, success, and happiness. The more consistently we practice this and the more consistently we are in flow, the easier and quicker the results. Conversely, the more we think, feel, and act in low vibration energy of fear, powerlessness, depression, worry, or grief, the more negativity we attract. There is a reason why bad things happen in threes because we are creating them through the power of our thoughts and expectations.

You will not be surprised after reading about my heart story, why I teach and coach on the power of our heart energy. It is the most powerful of the three electromagnetic centers in our body (the other two being our head or brain and our hara. The hara is an internal point in the abdomen below the navel and correlates to spiritually aligned action-taking). According to the HeartMath Institute, the heart has 60 times the amplitude of the brain, and its magnetic field can be measured many feet away. Our heart is our sixth sense, so when we communicate with others, we use not just our normal five senses; we engage the heart too. This explains why "magnetic" attractions or repulsions occur between individuals. The heart is also a gateway to the Divine within us and shows us a path to living a more intuitive, spiritual life, where we learn to co-create with Source energy.

There can be times in our life when our heart is speaking to us and seeks to awaken us from our unconscious slumber. I call it the awakening to our Dharma. Dharma from the Bhagavad Gita is all about seeking our life's purpose – a purpose that activates the expression of our unique gifts, talents, or learnings and uses these in service (for the welfare) of others. My heart has finally spoken its truth to me. I am born to make other women powerfully aware of their gifts and help them express these in a way that fulfills them yet empowers others too. Has your heart nudged you from your slumber? Have you been called to re-invent to re-ignite?

Esther Apoussidis is a highly qualified marketing professional, energy alignment coach, and holistic therapist. She empowers women, particularly those at a midlife crossroads, to break the habit of being stuck in life and find their true purpose. Esther supports her clients in creating their own unique Passionpreneur business to bring joy and expansion to their lives.

Esther has had the privilege of coaching women who have been stressed by financial lack and paralyzed by fear of making the wrong decision and taking the wrong fork in the road. Esther has helped her clients with a combination of energy and mindset work and newfound spirituality to trust in their own energy and instincts, to release what's no longer serving them, to align to a high energy frequency, and to trusting in a co-creative Universe to create clarity and to bring their plans, dreams and desires to fruition. When her clients start to do so and let go of the need to be perfect and in control, the miracles unfold…

If you want to take that leap of faith and start improving your life, you only have to reach out to Esther today. For readers of this book, Esther is gifting a free Energy Alignment Method session so that you can discover what is keeping you stuck in life and to find your path to living an unfettered life of unlimited potential. Please book here: www.energy-transformations.com/schedule. All fees will be exempt if you email Esther at esther@energy-transformations.com using the code UG4.

CHAPTER 14

THE POWER OF ENERGETIC BOUNDARIES

CREATING A PERSONAL SANCTUARY FROM THE WORLD

JAMES KAWAINUI

MY STORY

I love flying. Always have. Flying forces us to give up control. The moment we step onto that plane, we are putting our lives in some stranger's hands, having to let go completely of our safety and well being. We also don't get to choose who we end up sitting next to, especially if we're traveling alone. Will they be a talker or not say anything at all? Maybe they'll be someone who falls asleep and either slumps over towards you or snores. Or they'll ask you to get up to let them out and back into their seat multiple times during the flight. (One of the advantages of the window over aisle!) And a significant question (especially for women): Do I feel safe sitting next to this person? Last but not least, there's the challenge of being stuck in a metal tube, packed like a sardine, with a bunch of strangers for an extended time.

There can be so much anxiety and stress in flying that we can be frazzled before we even get on the plane.

Flying is a way of life growing up in Hawaii. The only way to get from island to island was (and still is) by plane. Years later, I flew in the Navy, logging over 1200 hours in the air, out over vast stretches of the Pacific and Indian Ocean, mostly hunting Russian submarines and communist block war ships. That's another story for another time.

A few years ago, I flew to Connecticut to teach a workshop and see clients, something I did a few times a year. Once airborne, I pulled out my laptop to go over the notes and outline for my workshop and spent the trip completely focused on the task in front of me.

Four and a half hours later, I felt the engines power back, and the plane dip down as we began to make our descent. So engrossed in what I was doing, I hadn't even looked up to notice the people around me, much less, the woman who was seated next to me. The flight attendant announced: "We will be hitting some turbulence as we make our approach; please ensure that your tray tables are in their locked position, your seats are upright, and your seat belts are firmly fastened."

No big deal. I was used to turbulence, having spent long hours in the air. I glanced out the window and noticed the dense cloud cover we were flying through. Totally relaxed, I sat back and closed my eyes in anticipation of landing.

Slivers of anxiety and fear began creeping into my thoughts. *Are we going to be okay? Am I about to die? What if I never see my family again?*

Wait a minute! Where was this coming from? What we were flying through wasn't that bad. A little bouncy but nothing compared to turbulence I've experienced in the past. Hell, the wings weren't even flapping! That's when you really know you're in for a rough ride. *Why do I feel sick to my stomach?* It didn't make sense.

Over the years, I've learned not to take the emotions or reactions I might be feeling at face value, especially if they show up suddenly. I checked inwardly to see if I could figure out what was happening. A shocked realization came over me. *This isn't even mine! Where did this come from? Who does this belong to?*

I started looking at the people around me and noticed the older woman sitting next to me for the first time. I remembered saying hi when we first sat down. She was a tiny Asian woman, barely five feet tall. Her whole body was visibly trembling, hands tightly clasped together. She prayed frantically, a rosary clutched between her fingers. *OMG!* I realize I forgot one of my cardinal rules. I left myself completely open and exposed energetically. I quickly reset my energy and cleared her energy out of my field. Very gently, I sent what she was feeling back to her. *This is your energy and not mine to carry. I don't need to process it with you, and I give this back to you. Thank you for the lesson.* I feel her fear and anxiety slowly ebb away.

We don't realize just how much other people's energies affect us daily. We assume the emotions we feel are our own, and most of us rarely question their origins. The reality is we are continuously affected by the energy of those around us, often in ways we can't even imagine.

Ever walk into a room and felt immediately at home or can't wait to leave? Have you ever met someone and taken an instant liking or disliking to them before they've said a word? What about being around two people having an argument and witnessing the furious exchange as it blasts through the air? You're not only feeling your emotions (your energy), you're also feeling theirs.

"I feel drained when I'm around a lot of people." I hear that a lot from the clients I work with. Maybe you're one of those who avoids large crowds, noisy malls, and even busy stores. You're not alone. Many sensitive people feel overwhelmed being out in public, choosing instead to stay at home or go out only when absolutely necessary. You've researched it or have been told by someone that you're an "empath." News Flash: WE ARE ALL EMPATHS! We all have empathic abilities. Some people notice them and use them. Others don't. But whether you're aware of it or not, they are there nonetheless.

Emotions are moving through your body all day long. Some of them are yours, some of them aren't. Joy, apprehension, fear, excitement, loathing, delight, boredom, anger, and jealousy are just a few of the possibilities. Our bodies are constantly processing these emotions as physical responses. This can look like tightness in your shoulders or a sick feeling in your stomach. A certain emotion may make you hold your breath, clench your teeth, or cause hyperventilation. Other emotions can trigger a release of tears or laughter. This is how your body processes the energetic flow of the emotions you are feeling, whether they are your own or emanating from those around you.

In order to not feel constantly bombarded by other people's "stuff," we need to learn how to strengthen our personal energy field. **When your**

energy field is weak and porous, everything and everyone affects you. It's not about shielding or protecting yourself. It's about having clear personal energetic boundaries.

The solution is not to hide from the world. The solution is to become empowered by learning to maintain your energetic field so you can live in the world, given any situation. We did not come here to be solitary creatures or to live isolated from each other. We came here to be in relationship with each other so we can learn and grow and make the world a better place.

To think you are at the mercy of and constantly being "bombarded" by other people's energy is the victim's mentality. This comes from a belief that everything is happening "to me" and that I have no power in the situation except to give in and allow it to happen. I say, NO! The stronger your personal energy field becomes, the less likely you will be impacted by the people or situations around you. There are ways to get stronger, take control, and change your situation, and I will be sharing one of these ways with you here.

I couldn't blame the woman on the plane sitting next to me for what happened. The cardinal rule I broke was not checking in with myself BEFORE I got on the plane to see how strong my field was and to power it up.

It's up to you to decide how much of the world you want to let in (or not let in) in any given moment and how focused and committed you are to knowing how and when you share your energy. To monitor and maintain the strength and durability of your energetic field is a game-changer. It will not only affect your overall well being and health in the long run; it will also affect your quality of life.

If you've had trouble managing the energy around you or didn't realize how much it has been affecting you on a daily basis, you're not alone. There is hope. I've helped people from many walks of life, including busy moms, career professionals, healers, and practitioners, including medical professionals in naturopathic and allopathic medicine. The following process will help you learn to strengthen your energy field so you can live and participate in the world with a level of ease and comfort you may have never experienced before. I have watched countless lives change when they brought this simple practice into consistent, daily use.

It takes awareness, diligence, and commitment to not allow the energy around you to affect your ability to live your life to its fullest. It's time to take back control. Are you ready?

THE TOOL

YOUR CRYSTAL EGG

CREATING A PERSONAL SANCTUARY FROM THE WORLD

Let's begin with a short meditation. Close your eyes and take three deep, cleansing breaths. Give yourself permission to slowly let go of your thoughts and focus on your breathing, making it as physical as possible. Feel the sensation of air moving through your nostrils. Feel the coolness of the air as it flows into the back of your throat and down into your lungs. With each exhalation, feel the warm air rising from your lungs as it passes through your nostrils. Feel the gentle rise and fall of your chest as your lungs expand and contract. Be present with your breath.

Find a rhythm that feels comfortable to you. Your breathing doesn't have to be deep or long, just something that feels normal and natural to your body. As you do, become aware of your thoughts. Notice them without judgment. As a thought arises, make the choice to bring your awareness back to your breath.

Become present to the rhythm of your body and what it feels like in this moment. As you do, you may become aware of sensations in your body. A clenched jaw, tight neck muscles, scrunched up shoulders, pain in your lower back. Again, as with your thoughts, notice them without judgment and give your body permission to relax. Feel your muscles unwind as you release the tension and any stored energy you may be holding on to. Give your breath room to expand and drop deeper into your body.

With eyes still closed, imagine in your mind's eye the presence of a very large, clear, quartz, crystal egg. It's upright, in front of you, about arm's length away. Take a few moments for the egg to settle into your vision as you become more aware of its presence. Your egg is brilliantly clear, as though you're looking through a plate glass window. If not for the slight shimmer around the edges, you may not have even seen it in front of you. What your egg looks like is entirely up to you. Your egg is taller than you are by about a foot, and about as wide as if you were to put your hands on your hips with your elbows pointing out to the side.

As you get used to the feeling of the egg and its presence in front of you, notice what it feels like. You may want to reach out and touch the exterior surface with your awareness. What does it feel like to you? Is it soft or hard? Smooth or rough? What color is it? Does it have a fragrance? Does it remind you of something familiar? This is your experience, so there are no wrong answers. Take a few moments to let your egg settle into your awareness and get comfortable with its presence. My egg has a bit of a pearlescent glow to it, and I feel, more than see, its presence.

Now, take two steps forward and step into the center of your egg. Your crystal egg is hollow inside with more than enough room for you to stand in and turn around if you want to. The crystal is the shell, and you are now its contents! Take a few moments to feel yourself inside your egg. I keep asking you to feel because I want you to notice the energy in and around your body. Do you sense any changes, even subtle ones? Experience the energy of not only the egg around you but of your energy as you stand inside it. What do you notice? What, if anything, feels different from when you were standing outside your egg?

Every time you step into your crystal egg, you're making a declaration to yourself and the world that this space, inside your egg, is for you and you only! Congratulations! You've just created an energetic boundary between yourself and everything around you, a safe space that belongs just to you. No one is allowed into your egg unless you give them permission! Your crystal egg will help you to both maintain and strengthen your energetic field so you won't feel bombarded by energy and situations outside of yourself.

You might ask, "Aren't I cutting myself off from the world? How do I move through the world and continue to connect with everyone around me?"

To answer this question, find a blank piece of paper and a pen or pencil. Draw a small circle in the center of a larger circle. The small circle is you; the outer circle is your crystal egg. Every time you step into your crystal egg, you are creating an energetic space around you, one that contains your energy and maintains it. The strength of your egg's boundary prevents people from entering your space without your knowledge. Everything and everyone else (energetically) is outside the circle that is your egg.

You continue to radiate your energy outwards into the world.

From the inner circle, draw arrows directed away from you to represent all the places and people you interact with and share your energy with daily: Your family, friends, co-workers, clients, or anyone else you encounter as you move through your day. Staying centered in your crystal egg may help you become more aware of how often you are pulled upon energetically. When your personal energy is continuously being given away, there is less available for you to live your life. As you become more conscious of this, you will choose how and when you share your energy. You share your energy out into the world by radiating it outwards.

Finally, draw arrows pointing towards your egg that stop at its outside edge. This is where everyone's energy stops. No one comes inside your egg unless you say so, period! I can't stress this enough. **With your crystal egg, you're creating a space that both contains and maintains your energy**. You get to choose now how you share it! You now have a buffer between your energy and everything around you. Your own personal sanctuary that goes everywhere you go.

Here's another way to see it that may be helpful. Think about driving in a car when it's raining. The car is your egg, and rain on the windshield is other people's energy. You see the rain, you know it's there, but it doesn't affect you. The car is the buffer. This is what happens when you are in your crystal egg.

Your crystal egg becomes a part of you. *You don't go anywhere without it!* Check in with your egg as part of your meditation practice or before you get out of bed in the morning. Make it a part of your morning routine. It's no different than taking a shower, brushing your teeth, or getting dressed for your day. The more you practice it, the easier it'll get and the stronger it will become. The process of checking in will become second nature and something you do automatically.

Check in with your egg periodically during the day, before you get out of your car, when you're at work or before you go into a meeting. Even online. Make sure it's there before you go into a store or when you know you'll be in a crowded room full of people. You may even want to check in before you make that phone call or have that difficult conversation with a client or family member. It becomes such a natural part of you that you begin to notice when it *isn't* there and around you. (For a more expanded in-depth understanding of the Crystal Egg practice, visit https://jameskawainui.com/crystalegg.

Your spiritual, emotional, and physical well-being is not only important; it's essential. Your Crystal Egg is part of that self-care. The stronger it gets, the more energy you will have to share with the people you care about and with anyone who may cross your path.

So the next time you're about to get on a plane, step into a grocery store, or are walking to the mall, check in to make sure you "egg up." In those moments when you are with your family and can feel your old patterns running, step into your egg and see what happens. Trust in your egg and relax, knowing that you're right at home.

James Kawainui is a Native Hawaiian Healer and an expert in chronic pain, trauma release, and clearing of cellular memory on the physical, emotional, and spiritual levels. James works with people all over the world, who often come to him after having tried **everything** to overcome their pain. Through his connection with his Hawaiian ancestors (Kupuna), James is able to read a person's energy flow and clear blockages from trauma, some of which have been passed down through generations. James' clients experience freedom, renewed hope, and a deeper connection with their body and soul on levels beyond what they imagined possible. James is also a trusted guide and mentor for his students, many of whom are corporate professionals and medical practitioners.

James contracted a rare and life-threatening form of polio at 8 months of age, which he overcame through the love and healing touch of his Grandmother. With his compassion and an understanding of pain at a deeply personal level, James has devoted his life to helping people live positive, productive, and pain-free lives.

To schedule a Healing Session, speaking engagements, podcasts, or for information on classes and workshops, contact:

Phone: 808-753-2486

Email: James@JamesKawainui.com

Website: http://jameskawainui.com/

Facebook: https://www.facebook.com/jameskawainui/

Instagram: https://www.instagram.com/jameskawainui/

CHAPTER 15

TAPPING INTO YOUR IDENTITY

BREAKING THE SHAME CYCLE FOR TRUE EMOTIONAL FREEDOM

MANDY MORRIS, LPC

"WHAT I TELL YOU IN DARKNESS, SPEAK IN THE LIGHT."

MY STORY

No one gets married, thinking it'll end in divorce. You get married, and you start to dream and dream big. I believed I had found my soulmate and that everything had brought me to this point of meeting "the one." Finally, my fairytale had come true, but it was the beginning of the most challenging years of my life, the most difficult seven years to be exact.

It all started about six months or so after our marriage, when things began to change. The snowball effect of darkness was just beginning to grow. It grew from no job ever being "good enough" for Kevin because most jobs were beneath him into the demon of his depression, spewing out negativity and hatred towards himself, me, the world, and God. This hatred made him believe the world was magically against him (he was somehow that important!). Being the one to bear witness to his "bad deal" turned into a cycle of me coming home, trying not to rock the boat, and always walking on eggshells. I'd do anything to try and ease his pain or uplift his mood; after all, I just wanted him to be happy, for us to have a happy marriage.

As the darkness grew, I had more nights of crying myself to sleep than not; the evenings were always the worst. After a long day of work, I called him and could discern by the tone of his voice whether it would be a good night or bad night. When I heard a negative tone in his voice, my stomach filled with knots. Sometimes I would sit in the car and just pray: "I don't want him to yell at me, I don't want him to hate himself or the world anymore. I just want to be enough, you know?" Enough that, no matter how bad the day was, at least we had each other. Enough for him to be happy when he sees me, to stop hating his life and everything in it. He told me there wasn't anything he wouldn't do for me and that I made everything better in his life. So why couldn't I make him happy? Why didn't my comfort, help, or presence console him? I just wanted him to get help. He was depressed, but with the anger and rage, he was not the person I used to know. It's hard to know what to do when you see the person you love falling apart but unwilling to get help. I couldn't make him happy. I was powerless to the darkness that grew.

There was only so much yelling, throwing things at the wall, breaking the dog's gate, threatening to burn every bible in the house, and threats of harming himself if I left, that I could take. I began to isolate myself, and I didn't have the energy for people. If I told anyone about his threats, his secret drug addiction, or the verbal and emotional abuse, he would tell me, "You'll make things worse for me, and you don't want to know what happens if you make things worse."

So I lived in fear, fear of coming home to his next existential crisis, fear of threats, and even worse, fear of finding him dead. *How did I not see the signs? Why did he change so much? Maybe I'm the crazy one?* These were the things I thought. He made pretty convincing arguments, and I always found myself being the one to apologize.

Of course, our marriage wasn't all bad. There were days, even weeks, that were the image of what I always wanted. He showed kindness and made me feel special again. I felt hopeful during these times. These times made me think that things were okay. He just needed to get treated for his depression, and then maybe our life could be more promising. It was easier to try to keep him happy and not rock the boat. I would do the grocery shopping, not forcing the issue of him getting a job, and not speaking up about my feelings, just to keep some peace.

A person can only lie to themselves for so long before going one of two ways: completely numbed and dead inside or starting to fight back. I tried the first method, and it didn't work, so I tried the other.

I'll never forget the first time I stood up to him. He was down in his "man cave", a.k.a. the dark, enclosed basement, spending another day doing nothing but playing video games. I told him, "I just want my husband back." That was followed up by him saying, "He's gone, and I don't know if he's ever coming back." Something came over me, something I've never really felt before, at least not like this. It was anger. I finally felt angry. That anger helped me feel the courage to use my voice. "I'm tired of the yelling, fighting, and constant negativity. Do my feelings not matter?" I think that was the first time I ever used a stern voice, although I was shaking as the words were coming out.

"Your feelings?!" he said, with a condescending tone and chuckle. "I'm the one who doesn't even know if I want to live! Everything is a fucking joke, and there is no light at the end of the tunnel." I continued to ask him to please get help and tell him that there could be a light. This sort of back and forth went the way it always did: me pleading for his well-being, him making some sort of threat, and then using guilt to make me feel bad for him. This was more confirmation that he found me not good enough to motivate him to want to live.

If he wasn't going to get help, I was, so I started therapy with John weekly. I started keeping a journal over the last year because I always felt I was crazy. John's office became my safe place. He started showing me the power and control wheel, the cycle of abuse, and information on manipulative tactics. As a therapist myself, I know these things. I know them! Why have I not made the connection? This is more than depression. He's been manipulating, gaslighting, and psychologically abusing me. And the veil began to come off. He hadn't changed; he was decomposing. The white veneer of the man I knew for years before we got married finally came off. He couldn't keep up the facade. He was breaking down, revealing his true self. I had to take back some control, so I started small by just getting back to taking care of myself again. I started coping with negativity better. I created a plan: a packed bag to keep in my car. Things were getting worse, but I was getting stronger. The next time he made me feel unsafe or threatened me, I would leave.

The next time happened, but this wasn't like any previous meltdown. To be honest, I don't remember all that happened; dissociating took over my brain. I was looking at myself on the floor, crying, completely frozen. Kevin was yelling, throwing things, and pulling out his hair. I thought to myself, *move. Just pick yourself up and go to the car.* It was like my entire body was lead. I couldn't move. At some point, the outburst stopped. I went to bed and did the usual, cried myself to sleep.

I almost canceled the breakfast I planned with my friend, but I decided to open up about what was going on. She convinced me to stay just one night with her. One night turned into three nights. I told him I didn't want to come home until we met with the counselor on Friday to develop a plan. I didn't know retaliation was around the corner.

There are moments in life that break you open. The night he came looking for me at my office was that moment. He showed up only to find I was not there. He screamed, destroyed his phone, and got back in his truck. His anger drove his vehicle straight into the Woodline and into a tree, totaling his pickup truck. He crossed a new line. This wasn't him trying to kill himself. His tantrum was a skewed attempt at trying to get me home. It wasn't until after I got his diagnostic report back that I realized I was dealing with a Narcissistic Personality Disorder.

I attempted couples counseling with him, but for those of you who know about personality disorders, they don't get "cured." Ultimately, I was able to get out. There were more incidents of trauma and attempts at restraining orders, but I eventually got out. My new home on Redemption Drive would be the birthplace of a new life and a fresh start.

After someone survives a trauma, divorce, or crisis, there is relief, but the after-effects can be just as debilitating. I didn't realize that once I started dating or even loving again, all my "baggage" would come back up. My old patterns of people-pleasing, trying to be perfect, managing moods, and feeling not good enough, did not magically go away.

I began my healing journey. I re-discovered my truth. As they say in the therapy world: what's wired together fires together. The conclusions I drew about myself during that time were that "I'm a burden if I don't have it all together," and "I'm messed up, not good enough, and I can't trust my judgment." I needed to unlearn this.

One of the biggest revelations in my own EMDR therapy was that I had this belief I had to be perfect to be loved. Love, for me, was conditional. This belief was formed through unhealthy relationships and reinforced in a traumatic way with my ex. I realized that when I'm free to be myself by quieting the chatter and pretenses in my head and letting go of what others think, I can let my true self out, and that self is lovable. When I think back to my younger self in pigtails, I would never tell that little girl she had to be perfect to be loved. When I think back about my younger self in my marriage, I would never tell her that she wasn't good enough or wasn't lovable. I would tell my younger self, "I'm sorry you have someone so sick in your life who doesn't see you for who you are." I'd tell her, "This might be your normal, but this isn't normal." I'd tell her, "This is not your fault. You don't have to try so hard." And I'd tell her, "Listen to your feelings because they're trying to guide you." I'd tell her that she deserves love.

On this healing journey, I had to abandon beliefs about myself that were never true from the start, beliefs so deeply ingrained they feel true, beliefs that don't feel authentic anymore. In moments of insecurity, they will pop up again, but they don't stay. I refuse to operate from lies about myself. As others reflect on the lies they believe about themselves, it will help them reconnect to their authentic self-truth: Forgiveness, grace, and worthiness. The tool I'll share will guide you in identifying the negative beliefs and lies running the show in your life, so you can begin to have freedom, relief, and the courage to be who you really are.

THE TOOL

You can listen to an audio version of the following exercise here:

Negative beliefs form from experiences in which we draw negative conclusions about ourselves. These beliefs stay stored in long-term memory (our subconscious). This is why we end up feeling the same way about ourselves over and over again. Maybe you find yourself saying, "That's just another reason why I'm not good enough," or, "I'm always going to be a failure." At some point, we get sick and tired of being sick and tired. This tool will help you create awareness of your negative beliefs, guide you into breaking the cycle of believing lies, and reconnect you to the truths about yourself.

Step 1: Think about yourself on a "bad day" and notice what the feelings are that usually exist on those days. Is it sadness, anxiety, anger, emptiness, or loneliness? And then, on a scale of 1-10, where 10 is the most distressing possible and 1 is feeling neutral, where do you find yourself on the scale during a bad day?

Step 2: Now that you've identified the feelings and the distress level, I want you to look through this list of common negative beliefs. When you come to one that connects with those feelings or distress levels you identified, write it down. A good way to know if a negative belief resonates with you is if it "stings" a little when you read it.

Negative beliefs:

I don't deserve love. I'm a bad person. I'm terrible. I'm worthless (inadequate). I'm shameful. I'm not lovable. I'm not good enough. I deserve only bad things. I'm permanently damaged. I'm ugly. I'm stupid. I'm defective. I'm insignificant. I'm a disappointment. I deserve to be miserable. I don't belong. I should have done something. I did something wrong. I can't be trusted. I can't trust myself. I can't trust my judgment. I can't trust anyone. I can't protect myself. I'm in danger. It's not okay to feel (show) my emotions. It's not safe to feel. I can't stand up for myself. I'm not in control. I'm powerless (helpless). I'm weak. I can't get what I want. I'm a failure (will fail). I can't succeed. I have to be perfect. I'm overwhelmed. I'm inadequate. I'm defective. I'm responsible (for everything). I'm a bad person. I don't deserve to exist.

Step 3: Pick the top one (up to three) that sting the worst. Now that you've identified the top negative beliefs, think back to a time in your life when you first remember feeling this way. If you can't think of a specific memory, it's okay to identify an age range. Write down the memory or age range. Take a minute to journal about how your younger self was feeling and the context of what was going on during that time.

Step 4: Imagine you get a moment to go back in time to that younger self who first started to form that negative belief. You look at the person, and with compassion, love, and your wiser self, you put your arm around the wounded you. What would you say to the wounded you that started to form that negative belief? For me, it would have been, "He's sick, and this has nothing to do with you not being good enough," or, "You are doing everything you can, and I'm so sorry you are hurting; a marriage isn't supposed to be this way." Sit with this for a moment. If you have trouble thinking of what to say to your wounded self, think of it in terms of someone you love or care about. If they went through what you did or felt that way about themself, what would you say to them?

Now, identify what was really true about your wounded self and how you wish you could feel about yourself now:

I deserve love; I can have love. I'm a good (loving) person. I'm okay as I am. I'm worthy; I'm worthwhile. I'm lovable. I'm deserving. I deserve good things. I'm fine (attractive/ lovable). I'm intelligent (able to learn). I'm significant (important). I'm okay just the way I am. I deserve to live. I deserve to be happy. I did the best I could. I can learn from it. I can be trusted. I can (learn to) trust myself. I can choose whom to trust. I can (learn to) take care of myself. I'm safe now. I can safely feel (show) my emotions. It's safe to feel. I'm now in control. I have choices. I'm strong. I can handle it. I'm capable. I can safely let go of some control. I can recognize appropriate responsibility. I can get my needs met. I can survive. I deserve to exist.

Step 5: It's time to reinforce that true belief about yourself. That negative belief was never true, and it's time to start seeing yourself for who you were and who you are. For this final part, you will be using an EMDR tapping technique to relax you, give clarity, and align the mind-body connection.

1. Put your hands out in front of you, so you are looking at your palms. Cross your hands so that your thumbs link and rest your thumbs on the small divot (soft spot) in the middle of the collar bone. Allow hands to rest and fan out on your chest. (Your hands are the butterfly wings.)
2. Hold your truth in your mind, that positive belief about yourself, and close your eyes.
3. Slowly tap hands on your chest, alternating left and right.
4. While tapping, breathe in through your nose and exhale through your mouth until you start to feel some relief. Keep holding that positive belief in your mind.

5. After about 20 seconds, pause your breathing and notice how you feel; notice the positive feelings, stay connected to only that, and begin tapping again.

You can do this as much as you need as long as it reinforces positive feelings and truth about yourself.

We must acknowledge our whole story, the dark shadows, and the light. Having the courage to acknowledge your whole story, the victories, and the shameful parts, is when grace and redemption can enter. They are free for the taking. It's time to take back your truth, your power, and your life.

Mandy Morris is a therapist, speaker, and mental health expert. As a public figure and champion for mental health, she strives to educate on the benefits of therapy and combat the stigmas that mental health is a weakness and change is unattainable. Mental health and wellness affect everyone, and she believes that stigma shouldn't get in the way of healing. Mandy has connected with major corporate companies, podcasts all over the world, and musical artists. She has served major platforms such as Apple, BET, Revolt, MTV, non-profits, and has worked alongside some influential mayors and governors to educate them in mental and emotional wellness.

As a Licensed Professional Counselor, Mandy integrates evidence-based approaches, positive psychology, and neuroscience into her work. Her gifts of empathy and compassion help guide her clients safely through healing. Mandy has a master's degree in Clinical Counseling and is a Certified EMDR Clinician & Anger Management Specialist. She is co-founder and co-clinical director of Mosaic Counseling Group. Mandy offers her expertise through her private practice, mental health courses, group sessions, speaking engagements, and social media presence.

No matter the situation, Mandy's goal is always to help others get to a place of growth, healing, and freedom. Mandy always does her best to spread the word that mental health is just as important as physical health, and change can be possible. Whether that's leading them to that through therapy, education on mental health, or through training, Mandy wholeheartedly believes that once you have the tools you need, you can live an abundant life worth living.

https://www.mandythetherapist.com/

Mandy Morris, LPC, EMDR Clinician
Licensed Professional Counselor
Certified EMDR Therapist
Certified Anger Management Specialist-II

CHAPTER 16

GARDENING

A CATALYST FOR INNOVATION AND HEALING IN THE NEW NORMAL

BY CEDRIC NWAFOR

MY STORY

Growing up in Cameron, we had six farms. We worked on the farms every day, and it was tedious manual labor. Despite all of this hard work, there were still days when we could not guarantee our next meal.

Fast-forward a few years later, I made it to the United States and met a group of farmers from Idaho who invited me over to learn about agriculture in the US compared to Cameroon. When I was in Idaho, I visited many farmers and learned about their daily activities. While I was on one of these farms, I watched a tractor till the soil for five minutes. At that moment, it dawned on me that the amount of work that tractor was able to do for five minutes was equivalent to what my family did for an entire week.

That tractor symbolized the resources, technologies, and expertise that exist in the US that could be connected to some communities in Africa and make a huge difference.

This led me to start an organization called Roots Africa that supports local African farmers by connecting them to the resources, expertise, and technologies in the US and Africa to help them come out of hunger and poverty.

No matter where you live, I encourage you to start your garden because your life may depend on it. Whether you live in a skyscraper or a basement apartment, creating a garden may be the first step you need to live a happy, fulfilled, healthy, entrepreneurial, and innovative life.

We have all heard the saying that "you are what you eat." This statement is as valid as the law of gravity, but even more accurate is the idea that we become what we grow and eat. So, what should we eat? In his book, *The Science of Being Well*, Wallace D. Wattles answered the question, what to eat?

> The answer is simple: Eat what nature provides. Nature provides every person precisely what they need for perfect health. Wattles explains thus: In ordering the affairs of nature, it has decided that human beings' food shall be according to the zone in which he lives. These are the foods best for the requirements of the climate. These are the foods that will be the freshest when a person eats them, and therefore most filled with the life force of the One Living Substance. In acquiring these foods, a person can be in the closest connection with the Principle of Life that created them. Hence, a person need only ask himself what food grows and lives where he lives.

It is difficult to follow this guidance due to the rampant centralization of our food system, making it almost impossible to eat local food. Most of the food we eat is sometimes grown from thousands of miles away. The two best ways to follow Wattles' recommendation are shopping at your local farmers' market and starting your own garden.

I would also change the introductory statement "you are what you eat" by saying, "you are what you grow and eat with intention." It is not enough to grow your food; the purpose you put in growth could be an incredible tool for healing and growth. When we eat healthy, nutritious food, we have a healthy body, and when we eat unhealthy food, the opposite happens. There are very few cause and effect relations that are as true as our eating habits and how they define who we are as individuals. It is true that when we take great care of our food, watering, and providing the right nutrients, we receive a healthy harvest. It is also true that the emotions and intentions we give our plants make the plants flourish and nourish our physical, mental, and spiritual being.

When we harvest food, it gives our bodies the nutrients and strength needed to grow and our minds the patience and hope that our hard work will be rewarded during harvesting. When we cultivate a plant with the intentions of love, peace, and health, we reap a harvest of love, peace, and health. Let every part you use in your garden symbolize an emotional or spiritual state you hope to attain. From the soils used in growing to the water used in watering, all of this could become intentional ingredients that would help you become a better version of yourself. So, if you have already decided to grow your garden, it should be easy to take this simple, intentional step towards holistic living and thriving.

Masashi Soga, Kevin J. Gaston, and Yuichi Yamaura, in their research work, *GARDENING IS BENEFICIAL FOR HEALTH,* provide robust evidence for the positive effects of gardening on health. With an increasing demand for reducing healthcare costs worldwide, the results presented suggest that gardening can improve physical, psychological, and social health, which can, from a long-term perspective, ameliorate and prevent various health issues facing today's society.

Many people believe that because gardening is inexpensive and anyone can do it, it is a top contender for the most-beloved activity during Covid 19. It's fun, pretty, and (sometimes) yields edible results. But what if it's also therapeutic? Throughout history, we evolved to live in a world surrounded by plants, so it makes sense we would thrive from gardening.

Throughout history, we have seen people like Steve Jobs and Jeff Bezos creating ideas and turning them into great organizations, and then we ask ourselves, how and where did they start? How did they think of something so big? We then assume they are unique people, and we do not have such powers, the ability to mobilize people, or the resources toward a cause. What we really need though, is a concrete example of "creating something out of nothing." There is no better way of demonstrating this point than starting your own garden. By simply using a seed, water, and a few other ingredients, we can create life and watch it blossom. The same way great minds visualize, mobilize, and garner resources to build great organizations. We need to see it and do it for ourselves to believe in this process. No book, lecture, or speech can give us the confidence of building something out of nothing more than the miracle of planting a seed and watching it grow.

There is no better way to grow something out of nothing than to grow your own plants. It is incredible to analyze the idea that one can grow something that will produce and multiply a hundredfold from a little seed.

Understand that how you plant a little seed that turns from something out of nothing is the first step of innovation and entrepreneurship and eventually building an organization.

The goal here will be to tap into your entrepreneur spirit by going through the process of looking at a little seed grow and changing from one form to another and eventually blossoming and producing a lot more.

This shows you how to start out of nothing and eventually become successful. Now, the question is, what will be the ingredients to become an entrepreneur, to become a problem solver, or to become an innovator? Once you figure what that is, you can achieve whatever you set your mind to get.

THE TOOL

HOW GARDENING IS HELPING THE WORLD IN THE NEW NORMAL

CONNECTION

During the pandemic with human contact craved, many have found having a conversation the difference between fulfilling our desire to belong or suffering in quiet desperation. Mathew Kelly, in his book, *The Rhythm of Life*, reminds us that one of our most important emotional needs is our desire for acceptance. Ignoring this need, especially during this trying time, means ignoring the best versions of ourselves. This crisis has laid bare our need to be connected to other humans leading us to seek new ways to build meaningful connections with others. Having a garden is not only an easy conversation starter, but also a way to tell other people that we care about something other than ourselves. In the worst-case scenario, you find someone who does not have a garden, where you share how much a garden has changed your life. In the best-case scenario, you find someone who has a passion for gardening, which could be the beginning of a new friendship or the strengthening of an old relationship.

BUILDING A SENSE OF HOPE

Plants have a way of instilling a sense of hope in us. There is nothing that guarantees that when we plant a seed, it is going to grow or bear fruit, but we believe and hope that our actions will be rewarded. In Cameroon, due to the lack of technologies to detect weather, we planned all of our crops, knowing there is a 50/50 chance we could lose it all. However, we choose to believe and hope for the best, even if the previous year was a disaster. This hope has stayed with me in everything I do. Without hope, it is easy to surrender to despair, causing our hearts to grieve and our bodies to show for it. Hope is the only way we come out of the current crisis and any other challenges we may face better than when we got in.

MENTAL HEALTH AND DEPRESSION

Experts have given a myriad of other reasons to start a garden today for healthy living. It helps us to get some exercise that could boost our physical and mental health. In times of social distancing, it gives us a great reason to go out and interact with nature in a purposeful and safe way. There is ample research that shows that gardens could help fight depression. In one study from Washington State University, 71% of people found a reduction in depression after going on an outdoor walk versus a 45% reduction by those who went on an indoor walk. It found that simply viewing a green space through a window or an LED screen can help people relax and reduce stress levels. Gardening also gives some level of control and confidence in a caustic world. It is in the growing that if we follow the right steps and take every persuasion, we will reap a bountiful harvest.

Now that you have so many reasons why you must start your own garden, here is how you start. Wait, remember that this garden is not just any other garden; it is a garden of love, peace, joy, harmony, healing, courage, abundance, hope, and whatever your heart desires. So before you start your garden, you must set the intention for that garden. Here is a step by step approach put forward by my colleague at the University of Maryland, Erica Smith, University of Maryland Extension, Master Gardener.

STEP 1- PLAN YOUR GARDEN

- Will you grow vegetables and herbs in containers or in garden soil?
- Will you create an in-ground garden, or perhaps use raised beds?
- Start small and expand when you are ready. A good starter size is 50-75 sq. ft.
- Grow vegetables that you like to eat and are expensive to buy. Some of the easiest vegetables are bush bean, tomato, cucumber, pepper, lettuce, summer squash, and leafy greens (Swiss chard, kale, mustard, etc.).
- Place taller crops on the north and west sides, so they will not shade shorter plants.
- Group plants by what season they grow in and how long they take to come to maturity. (This information is available on the Home and Garden Information Center website).
- Early, short-season crops, like lettuce, can give way to late season crops after harvest.

STEP 2- SELECT, YOUR SITE

- Your garden should be on level ground in a spot that gets at least 6 hours of full sun a day (preferably more).
- Avoid trees, shrubs, and buildings where possible.
- Make sure you have access to every part of your garden—include paths.
- Easy access to water is essential.
- Know your local animal population and fence as needed.

STEP 3- PREPARE YOUR SOIL

- Vegetable garden soil should be deep and crumbly, should drain well, and should contain plenty of organic matter.
- Have your soil tested to determine nutrient levels and pH and to be sure it is safe to plant in (fewer than 400 ppm of lead).

- Turn under or remove the grass sod but do not dispose of it as sod contains valuable topsoil and organic matter. You can also kill the grass by covering it with sections of cardboard or newspaper and then covering that with a two to four-inch layer of compost.
- Add at least two inches of compost on top of your soil and dig it in. Continue to add a thin layer of compost every time you plant. You can fill a new raised bed with purchased topsoil and compost.
- Raised beds may either be surrounded by an enclosure or built up with sloped sides and no enclosure.

STEP 4- PLANT YOUR CROPS

- Check the Home & Garden Information Center website to determine whether a particular vegetable is best direct-seeded in the ground or whether its seeds have to be planted indoors and grown to transplant size. You can buy seeds and transplants from local stores.
- If you buy seedlings to transplant, make sure they look healthy and are not so overgrown that roots encircle the bottom of the pot. Transplants raised inside your home or in a greenhouse should be exposed gradually to outdoor temperatures and conditions; this is called "hardening off.
- Transplant on a cloudy, calm afternoon if possible, and water well; handle plants carefully and make sure there is adequate room for the roots in the planting hole.

STEP 5- TAKE CARE OF YOUR GARDEN

- Water deeply around the base of your vegetable plants, as needed, to keep the root systems moist. Frequent, shallow watering is good for newly planted seeds—not mature plants.
- Water in the morning when possible. Use a soaker hose or drip irrigation system to reduce water use.
- Fertilize as necessary based on your soil test recommendations, fertilizer label instructions, and the needs of your different crops.

- Control weeds by laying down organic mulches, slicing or chopping weeds with a hoe, and hand-pulling. Start early, as soon as weeds appear.
- Support tomato, pepper, and cucumber plants with stakes or trellises to save space.
- Monitor plants regularly for problems; check out the University of Maryland Extension's resources for solutions. Learn to take integrated pest management (IPM) approach to any plant or pest problem.
- Vegetables and herbs can be grown successfully in Maryland gardens without chemical pesticides.

STEP 6 - HARVESTS AND ENJOY!

I would like to add here that, before you eat any items from your garden, express gratitude for yourself for growing said item, express gratitude to the item for growing as it should, and also extend gratitude to the entire seen and unseen process between planting and harvesting.

Afterward, you should state your intentions for the item you are about to put into your body. Tell it what you want it to do in your body, how it should nourish you and serve your other bodily functions. This might sound like an overstretch, but this is no different from vision boards and all the motivation we take in on a MONDAY MORNING as we gear up for a new week.

The matter of eating peacefully, happily, and full of gratitude must be emphasized, for it is our lot here on earth. You should seek to eat together with loved ones as often as you can. The aim is to eat happily whenever you eat.

A passion for agriculture and its people drives **Cedric Nwafor**, a social entrepreneur and public speaker who has organized, facilitated, and spoken at various African and US events. He is the founder of ROOTS Africa, a youth-led organization that combats hunger, poverty, and exclusion by connecting students and agricultural experts in the US to farming communities in Africa. While earning his bachelor's degree, he visited farms in Idaho and Maryland and Rwanda, Liberia, Cameroon, Ghana, and Uganda to learn different farm life and management approaches.

Along the way, Cedric became an agricultural evangelist, engaging African youth in civic affairs in both cities and rural communities. He believes that engaging the young generations in agriculture is vital to the African continent's future and the socio-economic well-being of its peoples. Cedric previously served as a Managing Partner of the Afrika Youth Movement, leading its five strategic committees, and as a Mentor and Advocate for Streetwise Partners, an organization supporting low-income populations. He was a 2016 nominee for the African Youth in Agriculture Award and served as a commencement speaker at his graduation from the University of Maryland College of Agriculture Natural Resources, when he received a BA in Agriculture and Resource Economics focusing on Entrepreneurship. He has co-created and instructed a Global Agriculture course at UMD and is now managing the university's Agriculture Innovation Program. Cedric is currently enrolled in a Non-Profit Leadership graduate program in the School of Public Policy. He is also a Do Good Accelerator Fellow and an Academy for Innovation Fellow. Cedric, born and raised in Cameroon, immigrated to the United States in 2010. He now resides in Maryland.

- Anon. 2007. *Ecotherapy: The Green Agenda for Mental Health*. Mind: For better mental health, London, pp., 36 pp.
- Kelly, M. (2004). The rhythm of life: living every day with passion and purpose.
- Wolf, K. (2018). Mental Health & Function.

CHAPTER 17

MANUAL MEDICINE

USING THE BODY AS AN ENTRY POINT FOR DEEPER HEALING

BY SHANNON BERK, MPT, CFMM

MY STORY

I am one of seven kids. Yes, I know, it was as crazy as it sounds. We didn't all live together in one house all of the time but when we were together it was complete chaos. Chaos still feels a bit like home. It was a "his, mine and ours" family with divorces and remarriages and more births. I ended up being the oldest of four living in our household most of the time, so although I am a middle child, I function like an eldest. Perfectionism was my favorite meal served with a heaping side of being a "good little girl."

Before age eight, I was able to fill the role of the second oldest to my big brother. He was two years older, and I thought he walked on water. I was pretty positive that I wanted to be him when I grew up. He had the greatest hair, he was athletic, loud, and fun, and usually got us into trouble, but the best kind of trouble. Most of the scars I have from childhood would definitely come with a story with him in it. I had the same haircut as he did, but growing up in the late 70s, I think most of us had the same haircut. The thing was, I was happy to look like him. I was even happy to wear his hand-me-downs. I was living in his shadow, but I thought it cast a beautiful glow. So when he played in a soccer league, so did I.

My parents made opportunities for all of us kids to play soccer regardless of gender. There were no girls' teams in that era, so I ended up being the only girl on the team every time. This came with lots of bruises. Regardless of the shin guards, I always came home with souvenirs of black and blue. One thing of note, I have always been on the smaller side of humans. It was always assumed I was easily five years younger than I was. I was the kind of tiny that gets you a child's dinner at a buffet when you're in high school. The world in which I played soccer was not one where being a tiny girl made you successful or safe. So when the coach put me on defense and said, "Now Shannon, I need you to stay on this white chalk line and don't move unless the ball comes to you. Your job is to keep that ball out of that goal right there. Got it?" Like a good little girl, I just nodded and did exactly what he said, all the while thinking, *FINALLY, it's about time someone stepped in and saved my life. I might have died out there.* So there I stayed on that white chalk line, forever and ever and ever. Our team was good, and there wasn't a lot of action at our goal. I was secretly delighted about that but also bored.

One particular day, on my chalk line, after the normal grass picking, cloud watching, goalie chatting, I was out of chalk line activities. Necessity being the mother of invention and all, I started walking the chalk line pretending I was a gymnast on the balance beam. I was thrilled to discover that my cleats made designs in the chalk. I could stomp patterns into the chalk, and the designs from the spins were a kaleidoscope of cool. I challenged myself to twirl and spin down the entire chalk line from one end to the other without "falling off my beam." I was in my bliss.

I was just completing my gold medal Olympic beam routine when the referee blew the whistle and brought me back into reality. As I was walking off the field to join the spectators and my team on the sidelines, I noticed the majority were looking at me and laughing. I was confused. *Are they laughing at me? Yes, they definitely are. Why? Is it because I am not good at soccer? Is my uniform on wrong? Is it because I'm the only girl?* I was mortified with no answers, so I hung my head and tried to crawl inside myself while the rest of the team ate their orange slices and drank their Capri-Suns.

After getting into the car, I let myself cry. I was always sensitive but had gotten messages from some adults that crying was uncomfortable for them and therefore tended to save it for quiet, solitary times. I still habitually do.

My mom picked up on my upset and asked, "What's wrong, Shannon?" After spilling all the embarrassment and hurt, she filled me in on what had occurred on the sidelines. The crowd noticed my solo dancing on that chalk line, made more obvious because there was no action at our goal and I was clearly more animated that day. The leaps were bigger, and the spins with arms uplifted and facial expressions of pure joy brought more attention, apparently. In my defense, I was not on that soccer field that day; I was competing for a gold medal, so of course, it was the performance of the season.

Luckily my mom and stepdad could see my place was not on the soccer field but in a dance studio, and that's where I ended up. It is probably one of the best things that has ever happened to me as I look back at my life. As my soccer career ended and my dance career started, my life took a turn for the better. I stopped living in my brother's shadow and having aspirations of being him and started living in my body and becoming myself. I discovered that my bliss was not on that field but in my body.

I never stopped searching for the bliss in my body, and I started searching for answers to how it all worked. I became a physical therapist, which landed me in classes at Michigan State Osteopathic Medical School in their continuing medical education program. From the moment I walked into the first class and heard the philosophy of osteopathic medicine, I was hooked. It introduced me to possibilities, philosophies, and paths I never knew existed before.

MANUAL MEDICINE

Manual medicine refers to an area of Osteopathic Medicine where the musculoskeletal system is manipulated using hands-on skills and techniques. Osteopathic medicine dates back to the late 1800s when Dr. Andrew Still became disenchanted with the medical practice of his day and created the following philosophy:

1. There is unity of the entire human system. It is considered as a whole, and each part affects every other part. You cannot separate the interconnectedness of mind, body, and spirit.
2. The healing power of nature. The body contains a self-healing mechanism. It possesses all things necessary for the maintenance of health and recovery from disease.

3. Structure-function interrelationship. Structure of a part or the whole governs its function, and function conversely influences the structure and form. (adapted from an excerpt in Greenman's Principles of Manual Medicine, fifth edition by Lisa A. Destefano)

The philosophy made sense to my logical brain and allowed me to appreciate areas missing from my understanding. The classes taught biomechanics and how the parts worked within the entire system, as well as instruction of manual techniques that would alter the physical form. All of that with a layered understanding of how changing the body affects the other levels of our humanity. It became clear to me that the body's (and the entire human's) natural state of being was perfect and complete wholeness and that my job as a practitioner was to find any barriers to its expression of that perfection. Healing was simply the process of removing barriers. That landed like truth to me.

This began to shift my thinking. What is wrong and how do I fix it? Became what is in the way of healing and why? It occurred to me, patients with chronic pain were not "unfixable," they just hadn't had anyone find the barrier to healing. The pain was the body saying the underlying cause had not yet been addressed.

MY HANDS = MY TOOL

Healing can occur naturally, or there can be assistants to healing. I am an assistant, and my primary tool is my hands. I alter the body with manual techniques and assist it by removing physical barriers. This could be me mobilizing a restricted joint or increasing flexibility of scar tissue using deep tissue work with the goal of finding its natural state of homeostasis or perfection. This is all with the knowledge that in doing so, every other interconnected part will be affected; mind, emotion, and spirit.

THE TOOL

You can be an assistant to your own healing and without any skill or technique training. One way to do this is through movement. Every time you exercise, dance, or stretch, you are altering your physical form. There is no way for all the other layers of who you are not to be altered simply because of the unity of the entire system.

Let's take, for example, a shoulder clock. It is a dynamic stretch technique that addresses restrictions in the thoracic spine or upper back. It is normally taught to patients to improve the ability to turn their body and reach behind them, lift their arms fully overhead, and even straighten up and reduce a stooped posture with rounded shoulders. In a purely physical sense, it's an effective exercise for improving motion and function.

Performing this stretch for the upper back can also affect the low back and the neck simply because of the interconnectedness of the physical parts. For your neck to rotate and look over your shoulder, your ribs and upper back must have the freedom to allow it. If your thoracic spine is restricted, when you turn your body to reach into the back seat of the car, all the rotation will bypass that area and rest completely on the function of the lower back. Eventually, the low back, needing to move way more than it should, becomes hypermobile. This causes irritation, inflammation, and pain. Your low back pain could be helped with a shoulder clock, addressing a restriction that is actually distant from your pain.

When you look at how the body can reflect the mind and emotions, you can start to see how a stretch can have far reaching effects. A stooped posture with rounded shoulders is commonly associated with feeling down or heartbroken, exhausted, having low self-esteem, and even disempowerment. It is not an accident that certain physical restrictions correlate with emotional states, and we can see them manifest in posture.

A dynamic stretch such as a shoulder clock alters the barriers to healing at a physical level, but because of the unity of our system, you can't avoid affecting the mental and emotional levels as well. The shoulder clock becomes an entry point into being empowered, improving mood, and increased energy. You are an integrated person, and there are no divisions between your physical, emotional, and mental bodies.

The shoulder clock can help you become aware of the interconnectedness of the parts of your body and may grant you access to healing on other levels. Every movement gives you similar access. Sometimes the most useful tool is a shift in how you see things.

THE SHOULDER CLOCK

This is called a shoulder clock because you will be lying on your side, and your arms will be functioning such that if I were to be on the ceiling looking down at you, your arms would be moving around an imaginary circle like the arms on a clock.

1. Choose a side to lay on, on the floor, or a bed. Bend your hips and knees (hips with at least 90 degrees of bending to protect your back) so that you stack your legs on top of each other. Extend both arms out straight, stacking them as well with palms touching each other. Support your head on a small pillow if need be; you do not want a side bend in your neck. You want your spine to be in a straight line from head to tailbone. This is your starting position.
2. To start the clock, you slowly slide the top palm forward. This stretches the back of the shoulder on the top arm and your upper back. Once your top palm contacts the floor, the goal will be to maintain contact with the floor with your hand.
3. In an arc, slide your palm along the floor up over your head. Your bottom hand stays still. From the clock analogy, the bottom hand is at 9 o'clock, and the top arm is sweeping from the 9 o'clock to the 12 o'clock position, palm down.
4. Around the 12 position, when your hand is up over your head, you will no longer anatomically be able to maintain the palm on the floor. At which point, you turn the palm to face the ceiling. The back of your hand is now in contact with the floor.
5. Continue sweeping the top hand from the 12 o'clock position, with the palm up, around in an arc to the 3 o'clock position. To have this occur, you must rotate your back and open your shoulder and chest. This tends to be a point where most people are tight and must raise their arm up off the floor. Do not push through pain at this point; it could cause an injury to do so.
6. Continue the arc, with the arm (palm up) from the 3 o'clock position to the 5-6 o'clock position. If you have complete motion in all areas of the spine, ribs, and shoulder, you should get to between 5 and 6. This should be when your arm gets close to your side body.

7. Reverse the arc all the way around the clock to the starting position. Repeat this ten times.

Things to note:

- You should do this on both sides of the body.
- If you find a "sticky" point, where the motion gets stuck or painful, stop and take two deep breaths into where you feel the restriction/ pain. If it does not release, then that is the endpoint for now. You continue with that as your stopping point for a few rounds. Typically the endpoint moves as you repeat it a few times.
- For a video demonstrating the shoulder clock with a more involved explanation as to its impact on the mind and emotions, go to my YouTube channel: Shannon Berk Physical Therapist.
- Credit for this stretch goes to MSU/ Mark Bookout, PT.
- Please consult your physician if you have any concerns about performing this stretch/exercise.

Shannon Berk is a functional manual physical therapist in private practice in Maryland. She has been in practice for 22 years and utilizes an integrated approach to treating the whole person. She is an adjunct professor at Michigan State University in their continuing medical education program, where she teaches osteopathy in the cranial field, levels 1 and 2. She was an integral part of the MSU team that created and implemented a certification in functional manual medicine. She is the co-founder and president of the non-profit Just In Power Kids that provides holistic support for children in Maryland going through cancer. Shannon loves reading, gardening, the beach, and being a mom and wife. You can find more information about Shannon at www.integratedwellnesspt.com, and if you want information or to get involved with Just In Power kids, go to www.justinpowerkids.org

CHAPTER 18

MYOFASCIAL RELEASE

THE BEAUTY IN RELEASING YOUR SCAR

BY SHELLIE MEKASH, CMT

Authentic healing, fortunately, can come to us in many forms. So much of how we are shaped and formed as people comes into play by how we were raised, who we were raised by, and what their experiences in life were. Influences surround us as we mature and grow to experience life on our own. It's here, in the experience sector, that we can be shown and attracted to a different way to do life. In my case, (maybe for you, too) a way I had no prior knowledge of. Alternative, holistic medicine gave me the gift of a lifetime and a gift to my spouse, my own children, and grandchildren as well. Authentic healing from decades of life happenings, pain, and dysfunction were the results for me. Oh, and most importantly, a whole new way to live! With awareness, there are many choices!

MY STORY

Waking up from surgery, the words I heard the surgeon say were, "We placed mesh from hip bone to hip bone and pubic bone to tailbone." *Huh? I didn't know that was a thing!* They had created a sling in my abdomen to keep the organs I had left there suspended. The result of doing all this internal work left me with a vertical scar running from my belly button to my pubic bone. At that point, I had no idea that this scar could bring about continued healing in and of itself.

Prior to this, I'd been on a downward spiral both physically and mentally for several years. Gone were the days of enjoying living the life of a busy, productive mother, farm wife, and employee. Instead, pain, drudgery, and sheer survival were the replacements.

My body systems were seizing up without any real known cause discovered. *How did this happen? How could this happen?* I was scared and confused. I felt pride in myself for being a seeker of knowledge and trying to figure out the pain and dysfunction that were plaguing my body. I reached far and wide to specialists and pain management programs in hopes of finding something, anything, that would help me. Even the world-famous Mayo Clinic! You know you're desperate when you hope for a diagnosis, no matter what the diagnosis is, just to have a name or label, something to identify with.

My thought process was: *If I could name this thing, I could go all-out fight mode and conquer it.* I didn't know then that fascial restrictions don't show up on an X-ray, CT scan, or MRI. It makes perfect sense now. At that time, I had a whole arsenal of prescription medications to combat the various symptoms plaguing my body. The pain was incredibly intense and unexplainable to the western medicine folks treating me the best way they knew how. Medications ranged from anti-anxiety to anti-psychotic to anti-seizure to narcotics, all prescribed to help me gain some sort of normalcy and function. But that's far from what happened. My day would begin by taking Oxycodone just to be able to take a shower and lift my arms to wash my hair. I continued to work, but barely. It was a far cry from how I had envisioned my life.

Fast forward to six months post-op. I was continuing to experience a significant amount of pain even while taking the plethora of prescribed medications to help with the various dysfunctions. I was also utilizing the sacral nerve stimulator implanted in my buttock for bladder retention. At one point, the doctors indicated I was on a trajectory for needing a colostomy. *How can this be? What can I do differently? What had I done to create this in myself? How much more can I take?* I had definitely reached a low point in my existence. Shortly after this experience, I decided to give it one more shot of being brave and made an appointment with a physical therapist in a neighboring town, who my friend said practiced a different kind of therapy.

That day turned out to be a fabulous day that will be etched in my memory forever. The day that I had my first myofascial release treatment. The thing that changed the most for me that very first day was that I felt hope. I had hope that there may be relief from all this pain and dysfunction, hope that I may be able to be the mom I so longed to be again for my daughters, and hope that there was something more to life than the way I was living, or rather, existing.

Through MFR therapy, I was able to unravel the stories held tight by my essence. I shed them physically, mentally, and emotionally by feeling into them and releasing them, thought pattern by thought pattern, belief system by belief system, layer by layer. It truly was a beautiful unfolding of my soul. Not only did I gain bodily functions again, but I was able to go off all medications. I am now living a life I had only dreamt of in the past. This transformation didn't happen all at one time, like a magician waving a magic wand, but rather, over 12 months from that very first appointment. And there is great beauty in that, as we grew together and saw that we could choose a different path for ourselves, as individuals and as a family unit. Today, we have a greater love and appreciation for each other and are continuing to grow and learn. Most importantly, we're letting go of what no longer serves us. Authentic healing isn't a one-time event but rather a process and a beautiful way of life.

THE TOOL

MYOFASCIAL SCAR RELEASE

When I work on releasing the scar I talked about earlier, the belly button to pubic bone one, there is ample opportunity to feel into the depths of that scar. After all, it is a bit long! But don't be fooled; a small laparoscopic scar can have far-reaching restrictions felt very far from the source, too. For instance, with my vertical abdominal scar, I have felt releases, pulling sensations, and melting sensations all the way up into my right shoulder. In addition to that, bladder function increases after I have done scar releases there. Think of this scar as having restrictions running down and around the bladder, not allowing it to compress and empty, restricting its movement. Herein lies the beauty of the scar release.

Before we start out placing our fingertips on our scars, it's helpful to understand fascia, the tissue inside your body that Myofascial Release is based upon. Fascia (pronounced FASHA) is a three-dimensional, head-to-toe system of connective tissue that surrounds and connects every single cell of every single organ, nerve, blood vessel, muscle, bone, etc., in your body. Visualize a web underneath your skin. It's a super-highway for information and energy, a liquid crystalline matrix that plays a role in consciousness.

When fascia is healthy, it can move in any direction and maintain a fluid, mobile state. There are many different reasons that fascia becomes dehydrated and/or restricted, including physical or emotional trauma, surgery, injury, inflammation, or repetitive posture, or any combination of those. Restrictions in the fascial system can cause intense pressure to build up around your body's internal structures, which can, in turn, create tightness, pain, and dysfunction. These restrictions can run vertically, diagonally, or horizontally. There is no set, prescribed pattern. Each individual has a separate internal environment. When these fascial restrictions are released, one can return to homeostasis and a pain-free, active lifestyle.

When a scar is involved, we may think of it as just the skin that has healed, observing variations from a smooth, thin line to a ropey, thick, raised adhesion. Our mentor, John F. Barnes, explains, "a scar is the tip of a fascial iceberg." Just as an iceberg reaches into the depths of the water (mostly unseen), so it is with the fascial iceberg creating fascial restrictions that can be responsible for organ dysfunction and reduction of movement from structures within the body. Restrictions from these scars may be felt as pain, numbness, or tingling in areas higher or lower than where the scar is located and have a tentacle-like pulling or tugging effect on surrounding tissue and joints.

John F. Barnes Myofascial Release (MFR) uses a mind-body-spirit approach to treat fascial restrictions and is a whole body, hands-on therapy. As practitioners, we learn how to perform releases on clients and educate our clients to perform releases on themselves to alleviate pain and dysfunction.

Let's get started by doing a MFR (myofascial release) scar release on your own body. To clarify, the age of the scar is immaterial. Sometimes we've even forgotten about a scar or a surgery, but there is opportunity there for releasing and healing! If it is a new scar, check with your medical professional about when it is safe to do this.

PREPARING YOURSELF

- First, let's begin by centering and grounding ourselves.
    - Make yourself comfortable in a seated position or by laying down.
    - Take a slow, deep breath into your lower belly and exhale, following your breath in and out.
    - With each exhale, allow yourself to relax and soften a little more.
    - Repeat three times.

THE TECHNIQUE

- Locate a scar on your body that you can comfortably touch with your fingertips.
- Place your fingertips along the line of the scar. Depending upon the length of the scar, one fingertip from each hand or all four may be used.
- Make a note of how you feel in relation to that scar.
    - What feelings does it bring up for you? For some, it could be a memory or reminder of a trauma or accident, or injury that you may have put aside or buried.
- Give yourself permission to feel, making no judgment of what comes up.
- Now make a connection with your fingertips and the surface of the scar.
    - Does the scar feel taut or free, or raised or rough or smooth? Hot or cold? Fat or skinny? Tender or numb?
    - Take a moment to check in and notice what you feel.
- Gently allow your fingertips to sink into the scar until you feel a change in consistency or a barrier.
- Keep your awareness focused on that area, as it will increase the energy.
- Slowly move your hands/fingertips apart from each other until you reach resistance and hold that position, continuing to sink in deeper as the body releases.

- If it feels right, say to yourself, "I let go of all that no longer serves me."
- Hold this position for three to five minutes (longer is good).
- As you experience a softening of the tissue (releasing), allow your fingertips to sink in even deeper and expand. Never forcing or leading.
- I encourage you to be open to feeling throughout your whole body, as restrictions can and do run freely within our internal body. Be curious. And at the same time, be gentle with yourself.
- If your body wants to move in any way, tremble or shake (unwinding), allow yourself to be open to the experience and the beauty of MFR.
- Repeating this exercise often will continue to help you release the restrictions deep within your body, mind, and soul.

Once finished, allow yourself time to process your experience and make a note of how you feel in your body physically and emotionally. Keeping in mind there is no right or wrong way to experience this. Be easy with yourself and be open to expressing gratitude to the magnificent vessel that is your body.

There is beauty in releasing your scar(s). As you can imagine, it's very much an individual experience and one that may be different each time you do it. The benefits can definitely be far-reaching and well worth the time spent.

To obtain a free audio version of this exercise, go to www.shelliemekash.com.

Shellie Mekash, CMT, is an expert holistic bodyworker specializing in John F. Barnes Myofascial Release, Reiki Master, and dabbler in Qi Gong and Healing Touch. Her passion is helping others see that there are other ways of healing in addition to traditional western medicine. She compassionately helps men, women, and children of all ages achieve relief from chronic pain and stress with a powerful, effective, mind-body approach.

Shellie and her husband reside in rural Minnesota on their family farm. She is the proud mom to four beautiful daughters and five fabulous grandbabies. In her spare time, she can be found supporting their athletic endeavors or in the great outdoors enjoying the beauty that surrounds us and soaking in the magnificence of new life and expanding family.

Start your journey to health and joy today. Connect with Shellie to begin or dive deeper into your healing journey by visiting her website as www.shelliemekash.com. With awareness, you have a choice!

CHAPTER 19

REBRANDING ALCOHOLISM

A TOOL FOR HEIGHTENED AWARENESS AND EARLY DETECTION

BY SUSAN GAERTNER

MY STORY

"Don't move," she warns and darts behind me. I freeze. A virtual statue—feet planted; left arm up-stretched; back arched and chest thrust forward. My neck twists at a 90-degree angle as I stare, transfixed, over my right shoulder; my bare left breast locked tightly in a mechanical vise.

"Don't breathe," the technician calls out again. She is poised behind a protective screen, and I follow her instructions to a T. As if my life depends on it. When she gives the all-clear, I release my breath, and the vise releases my breast. The tech apologizes for the obvious pain, but I tell her I'm fine. I don't complain. I never complain. In my mind, the tighter the squish, the better the image. *Onward to the right breast!*

I've never been diagnosed with breast cancer, but I know the fear associated with abnormal mammograms, biopsies, and a decades-old surgery to remove atypical cells.

My mother never told a soul when she first detected her lump. I'm not sure why. Was it fear? Denial? Shame? She herself wasn't sure. By the time she was diagnosed, the rather large lump had turned out to be an aggressive cancer that invaded her lymph nodes. Ultimately, she did well with her mastectomy, and the cancer never returned. Two of her younger sisters were diagnosed with breast cancer as well, so I remain vigilant. Breast cancer is a progressive disease, and I'm determined to uncover any prowling cancer cells as early as possible. But isn't this the beauty of awareness and early detection?

I contrast breast cancer with another progressive disease—alcoholism. Whereas breast cancer awareness is regularly promoted through marathons, events, and fundraisers, alcoholism is stigmatized and mocked. While countless products and brands embrace the color pink to encourage early detection, society is stuck on shaming alcoholism and those who have it.

Dr. Ben Carson joked about alcoholism in his campaign speeches as a candidate for President of the United States in the 2016 Republican primaries. (Keep in mind, Carson is also a world-renowned medical doctor.) The audiences reportedly roared with laughter.

Even Alcoholics Anonymous, the infamous global organization that helps those with a desire to stop drinking, carries the weight of shame within its very name. But I'm not just pointing fingers, because I too, am guilty of attaching derogatory labels to this disease. *Just keep reading.* The stigma runs deep, impeding awareness, early detection, and life-saving diagnoses.

A completely random series of events prompted me to question the potential for this disease in my own life. "Could this be alcoholism?" With no help from society, I developed my own heightened awareness of alcoholism. Eventually, I determined that I was in the early stage of this disease and could stop its progress. Based upon my own success, I developed a 3-step tool for awareness and early detection of alcoholism, which I include at the end of this chapter.

But first, let me take you back to that random (and lucky) series of events that prompted me to question the potential for this disease in my own life.

THE PITTSBURGH 'HUN'

My husband and I were headed for divorce; I just didn't realize it yet. I only knew that my once happy home had become inundated with sadness and anger and that I needed an escape. So I packed up the van for a long weekend in Pittsburgh, my childhood hometown, and proceeded to cry my way across the state of Pennsylvania.

I'm just a few miles from my mother's apartment when I decide to take a quick detour. With the city skyline in the distance, I cross the 40th Street Bridge and head to the Paddy Cake Bakery.

"Anything else, hun?" The older woman behind the counter awaits my response as she wraps the apricot pastries (my mom's favorite) and twists string around the white boxes. "No, thank you," I reply as I pay for my purchases, then hurry toward the exit. "Have a good day, hun," she calls after me.

The next morning my mom and I are seated together in a small booth, having breakfast at the local Eat'n Park Restaurant. "More coffee, hun?" The waitress tilts her glass pot in my direction, forcing eye contact. "Yes, please," I nod. "Thank you." She tops off my cup and moves on to the next table. I close my eyes and fight back tears. This woman's smile has pierced my fragile emotional state, and my body soaks up her 'hun' like a dry and brittle sponge.

On my third and final day of this visit, I'm food shopping for my mom. "Find everything you need, hun?" The young cashier glances towards me as she bags my groceries. I'm sad and desperate. My world is collapsing. I'm old enough to be this young woman's mother, and I cling to her 'hun' with every ounce of my being.

I knew that I'd receive the love and support of my family during this visit, but who were the women? Who were the three women, all strangers to me, who rallied to nurture me when I needed it most? What was that special connection? (Years later, as I retold this story to a friend, she smiled knowingly and summed up my experience: "The sisterhood.")

I feel stronger during my return trip to Virginia. I'm actually smiling as I roll along the Pennsylvania Turnpike, still basking in those back-to-back Pittsburgh 'huns.'

When I arrive home, I Google "women and friendship." My search reveals the perfect book, *Let's Take the Long Road Home*, by Gail Caldwell. It's a beautiful story, a memoir of friendship between two women, and Caldwell's writing confirms my belief that women share unique bonds. I finish the book, and I'm left longing to know more about the other half of their amazing friendship.

So I wasn't looking for a book about alcoholism on the day I reached for this best-selling memoir. My only objective was to learn more about Caldwell's friend, Caroline Knapp, who also happened to be a writer. She had written multiple books. But on that day, *Drinking: A Love Story* was her only available title in the bookstore.

Her writing was stunning. I particularly admired the words she used to describe drinking—she captured the pure joy, the unique emotions and sensations; the exquisite taste. Knapp called it love. I liked beer. But when I entered the pages of this paperback, I realized it was something more. I, too, was in love.

Still, there was a dark and dangerous side to her drinking that I didn't recognize. And I didn't share. I didn't understand blackouts or drunkenness. I did not identify with stories of falling down or hiding liquor bottles. None of that was familiar to me. And I began to wonder—*why is she a raging alcoholic and I'm not?* Page after page, this question repeated itself in my mind.

And finally, the answer hit me. Caroline Knapp had loved drinking since the age of 14. I was in my late 30s before I began to love the taste of beer. I rationalized that Caroline Knapp was a late-stage alcoholic, and I was still in the early stages of the disease. *It's just a matter of time. In time, I will become a raging alcoholic, just like Caroline Knapp.*

I sensed immediate pushback. *Could I* ***really*** *be an alcoholic? Would that mean I couldn't drink anymore?* This thought was more than I could handle. *What would life be like if I couldn't have a cold beer after cutting the grass on a hot July day? Who would I be if I couldn't share a drink with friends at an outdoor café?* These were serious questions. *And what about traveling? Would I never again relax with a beer at an airport or enjoy a beer on a flight?* All of this was unthinkable.

Soon, panic set in. Suddenly I was defending myself against the possibility of this disease, or more likely, the stigmas associated with it. I couldn't *be* an alcoholic because I wasn't a bad mother. Or a bad employee. Or a bad neighbor. The list goes on and on. *Thank you, society, for perpetuating shame about a progressive disease!*

I took a deep breath. If I *did* have alcoholism, I would share Caroline Knapp's future. And I did not want that future—for my children or me. I needed a definitive answer, once and for all—do I have alcoholism?

I began a deep dive, a chronological search of my life. I was looking for clues or red flags, memories or emotions, anything that might point to signs of alcoholism. Now, to be honest, I wasn't looking for confirmation that I had alcoholism; quite the opposite. I was in search of proof, evidence that I didn't. *You're fine. Stop worrying. You're not an alcoholic.* That's the self-diagnosis that I was shooting for. But there was one thing I knew for sure. Caroline Knapp had raised the first flag.

MAPPING THE RED FLAGS

FLAG 1 (LOVE)

Caroline Knapp taught me that I didn't like beer. I loved it. And love became the first flag. If I continued to drink, I, too, would become a raging alcoholic. It was only a matter of time. (This was when I developed the terms "early-stage" and "late-stage" alcoholism.) Although this thought was unnerving, it was not enough to declare myself an alcoholic. And I moved forward with my search.

FLAG 2 (GENETICS)

I looked for clues in my genetics. My parents and grandparents—all birthparents—provided important information.

My father had alcoholism; but what about his parents? I didn't know much about my dad's mother. She had died before my father married, so I couldn't factor her into my genetics equation. I didn't know much about my paternal grandfather, either. He had died before I was born. But I remembered hearing stories about the men at my dad's church, drinking beer in the social hall after Sunday mass. Based on that memory alone, I marked him as a maybe.

My mother did not drink at all. I grew up with both of her parents, so I knew that my maternal grandmother did not drink. But my maternal grandfather did have alcoholism.

I rated my genetics a 50/50 and marked this as another flag. My search continued.

FLAG 3 (SO IT WASN'T SHEER WILLPOWER?)

Right after college, I joined the Peace Corps. There was one particular memory that stood out with respect to alcohol. Was it a potential flag?

I was sitting at a table with two other female volunteers and three local men. We were guests in this home, and the hostess offered a warm, homemade alcoholic drink. To be polite, I accepted. It tasted horrible, but I knew the men were watching for our reactions. They assumed that these three young American women could never handle the taste and strength of this liquor, and I decided to prove them wrong. Round after round, I kept drinking. I hated the taste of each sip, but I enjoyed the shocked expressions on the men's faces. My Peace Corps friends couldn't keep up, and both women became violently ill that night. But I was fine. It was as if I had been drinking nothing but water.

I always believed that it was sheer willpower that allowed me to drink a ridiculous amount of alcohol that night. But after reading Knapp's book, I wondered if it was something else. Knapp wrote that alcoholics could build up a tolerance for alcohol, enabling them to drink greater and greater quantities. Since I was not a regular drinker at that time, tolerance was an unlikely explanation in this situation. Still, I wondered. *Perhaps I was **born** with high tolerance.* And that rationale became the third flag.

FLAG 4 (THE NAGGING QUESTION)

I continued to examine my life, year by year, and there was nothing unusual throughout my 20s and 30s—no red flags. And then I remembered a nagging question that came up in my early 40s.

When my first son was born, I stopped working and became a stay-at-home mom. It was the first time ever that I kept alcohol in my refrigerator, and I began to enjoy a beer at the end of the day. I remembered a moment when my son was about two years old, and I worried that he would have memories of mommy holding a green glass bottle while cooking dinner. And so I began to pour my beer into a coffee cup. At the time, I wondered, could this be a sign of alcoholism? It was a nagging question. And that nagging question became flag number four.

FLAG 5 (NUMBING THE PAIN)

Then came my divorce. It was awful and painful, and I drank to numb the pain. It raised another flag, but in my mind, the evidence was circumstantial. *Wouldn't anyone drink to numb the pain of divorce?*

(This was the first flag to be raised in real-time; it related to a current life event rather than a past memory. I now was watching for real-life indicators rather than examining past events.)

FLAG 6 (GUT PUNCH)

On this March day, my sisters, my children, and I visited my mom in Pittsburgh. Cousins from my father's side of the family were there as well. We did not often see these cousins, and I thought it would be a wonderful opportunity to learn more about my paternal grandmother. When I began to ask questions, one cousin laughed and remarked, "She loved her beer." GUT PUNCH. I had a physical reaction as if my cousin had punched me in the gut, knocking the wind out of me. I couldn't speak, and I'm sure the blood drained from my face. *Beer was my drink! This was not a good sign.* I was already living with five flags for alcoholism, and I certainly didn't need this additional link. Every single day after that visit, I woke up with the sensation of that gut punch. Flag number six! But still, not enough to declare alcoholism.

FLAG 7 (ICED TEA)

One November day, eight months after the gut punch, I made plans to meet a dear friend for lunch. I felt giddy driving to the restaurant—as a single mom with two young boys, I didn't often find myself with a free Sunday afternoon. I looked forward to my friend's company, a good political conversation, and lots of laughter. But foremost on my radar that day was my first sip of an icy cold Heineken.

We requested a booth toward the back of the restaurant—both of us particular about restaurant seating. The waitress approached to take our drink orders. Glancing up from the menu, my friend casually requested an iced tea. *An iced tea? What the hell? Is she kidding?* My mind was reeling with questions.

The waitress looked my way. "I need to have a beer," I said to my friend, chuckling and just a bit annoyed. "Of course," she responded, smiling.

Halfway through our meal, the waitress checks in, and I order a second beer. Now it's time for my friend to redeem herself and order a beer. But she orders a second iced tea. I stare across the table in disbelief. *I can't do that. I cannot order an iced tea.* And with that, I knew. It was alcoholism. Over the past 18 months, I had accumulated six flags. Flag number seven provided the definitive answer. And that Heineken was the last drink I ever had; it's been almost nine years now.

THE TOOL

The following 3-step tool offers a pathway to greater awareness, detection, and diagnosis of alcoholism. I utilized this technique in my own early-stage self-diagnosis, and I was able to stop the progression of this disease dead in its tracks.

STEP 1: A PROGRESSIVE DISEASE

Alcoholism is a progressive disease. Your single goal in Step 1 is to accept this statement as an unquestionable fact. You must believe, with every cell in your body, that alcoholism is a progressive disease that only gets worse over time.

Step 1 is non-negotiable. This tool will not work for you if you do not completely accept the statement above.

STEP 2: NO ONE IS IMMUNE

No one is immune to this disease. You must accept this statement as a pure and unquestionable fact. Here's another way of stating it: "There is nothing special or unique about you when it comes to alcoholism. There is no special shield or armor that can protect you, or anyone else, from this disease."

Step 2 is non-negotiable. This tool will not work for you if you do not completely accept the statement above.

STEP 3: MAP THE RED FLAGS

Do not move on to Step 3 unless you have completed Steps 1 and 2 of this tool.

"Could this be alcoholism?" In Step 3, you will not run from this question. You will actively search for answers. You will stare down society's stigmas and reject derogatory labels because you are protecting yourself from a progressive disease to which no one is immune.

You are on a chronological search for clues—memories in your past, as well as behaviors and events in your present life—that raise a red flag. You will be vigilant and constantly aware. It was the accumulation of flags, and the constant awareness that allowed me to detect this disease at an early stage. Still, it took seven flags and 18 months before I would stop drinking. Each person's journey will be unique.

I still have alcoholism. But I remain vigilant. Taking action was key to stopping the progression of this disease. And with constant awareness, I'll remain in life-long remission. Pretty cool stuff! But isn't that the beauty of awareness and early detection?

Susan Gaertner is a communications strategist and owner of When a Woman Starts Over, LLC, a communications consulting firm specializing in women's rights, reproductive rights, and gender equity.

Susan is an author, speaker, and gender equality activist. Prior to founding When a Woman Starts Over, she worked for 20 years as a communications strategist for research institutions, non-profit organizations, and government agencies, including U.S. Agency for International Development (Women in Development Office), and WorldWIDE Network (Women in Development and Environment).

For more information, visit www.WhenaWomanStartsOver.com. Follow When a Woman Starts Over on Facebook, Instagram and Twitter. Follow Susan on LinkedIn and Clubhouse.

CHAPTER 20

LEGACY WORK

LIVING LIFE WITH INTENTION AND PURPOSE

HEMALI V. VORA, MPT

MY STORY

My dad, sister, and I were sitting around the family room with the television on. It was late at night, and kids, hubby, and Mom had gone to sleep. We could hear the TV in the basement where my brother was awake and lying on a hospital bed. It seemed as though the past six months were going in slow motion for us. Our whole family was drowning in one health problem after another, very often attempting to come up to gasp for air, but suddenly another wave would suck us right in.

My dad was a stickler about "Early to bed and early to rise," yet he stayed up late with the television turned on. Most of the nights, we sat around in the family room in our own thoughts, silent, as though waiting for something to happen. One such night in early January of 2010, he was just discharged from the hospital with a prescription to use oxygen at all times. He sat in his regular spot on the yellow down sofa on the left side, with his legs extended on a large soft, red, square ottoman. There was a constant humming sound coming from the newly-placed, large oxygen machine to his left. One end of the long wire went in his nose and the other attached to the machine. The wire was so long that it extended to the bedroom upstairs where he slept. My sister was sitting on the right side of the same sofa and I was cuddled up across in a huge, red, bulky chair. All three of us sunk into our respective spaces, with throws warming and comforting us.

Earlier that day, at work, I remembered hearing a social worker asking a patient about his advance directive and I attempted to ask my dad, stumbling, "Dad, what's your wish? I mean medically, what would you like us to do in case you are not able to make decisions. What are your wishes medically?"

Dad thought for a second and said, "I don't want to be hooked up or survive on machines." I could see he was still processing this question and deep in thought. We all went into our own deep thoughts, staring at the TV and pretending to watch whatever was playing. *Isn't it everyone's wish to die in their sleep? I guess it would be peaceful. And no one wishes to survive on these machines forever. Death is such a mystery; it's like uncharted territory; no one wants a painful death. It is scary to think about it. Will we suffer? It's scary to think we would leave all of this behind. What is on the other side?*

My dad interrupted my thoughts by announcing, "I would like to donate my body to the medical school or a facility. Once I'm gone, I don't need my body, and I would like my body to be useful. How can I donate my body?" My sister and I were surprised and fascinated by the idea and at the same time, thought of our experiences in our anatomy and physiology class. We discussed how some students while learning on cadavers, name the body, joke about it and their private parts, and make up stories about them. My dad wasn't buying that explanation. "It's just a body, not me," was his response.

All of a sudden, he sits up, with excitement, gleeful like a little kid that found a hidden treasure, smiling from ear to ear. "Do you know what this means? I am finally going to meet my parents and be with them. Wow, I wonder what it would be like; I can't wait." He probably saw our faces and read our minds. "You know God just needs a name or an excuse or a reason to take you, and mine is pulmonary fibrosis. When it's time to go, it's time to go." Just matter of fact. He continued, "Will I recognize my parents?" He was two years old when his parents died. He lived with different family members and finally with his six elder siblings. All had transitioned in their early 60s. He was truly raised by a village of loving and caring people.

My aunt had transitioned six months before. She was his last surviving sibling. Seeing her motionless, he said, "I am next." The next month, he was diagnosed with pulmonary fibrosis with no known cause, no cure, and five to seven years of life expectancy. Dad was very active, didn't drink or smoke, exercised daily, worked full time, and months before the diagnosis, volunteered a couple of nights a week in the hospital ER. Yet, he was deteriorating. I guess that's the effect of giving up on life; to feel that you are next to go.

On January 31st, 2010, Dad was in the ICU semiconscious, unable to respond, his room overflowing with family, friends, and people he loved, adored, and cherished. As my sister whispered in his ear, giving him permission, "Dad, we love you; it's okay to let go, we will be okay," tears rolling down the side of his eyes, he took his last breath. His body was accepted by a medical research facility in Baltimore, Maryland. Once they were done taking the organs they needed, they cremated the body, and ashes were mailed to us. That gave us comfort and closure.

As the news of Dad's transition reached India, all his family, friends, neighbors, and acquaintances wanted to hold a prayer gathering for him within hours. As we were in the US, my cousin in India organized the gathering. My mom, brother, sister, and I dressed in white Indian outfits, huddled around the laptop at 4:00 am, turned on Skype, and were able to participate in the prayers and tribute given in my dad's honor. There was an overwhelming outpour of love and support; hundreds of people gathered and spoke about dad, what he meant to them, and how he changed their lives. Some told stories of how he helped them get a job or a college admission. Some talked about how he helped find them a place to live, start a business, or recruit clients. And some spoke about how he helped them get married and provided food. One neighbor narrated her story of how she had taken poison as a teenager, and he rushed her to the hospital and saved her life. She is married with kids and grateful to get a second chance at life. We lived in the US for 20 years, and yet he was in touch with all of them. His final act of giving was of his body to the medical field. I was so proud of the man my dad was and the impact he had in his short life. His life was filled with struggles, hardships, challenges, life-shattering betrayals, and losses at an early age, yet he didn't let that affect his purpose in life to help and feed people around him, to keep smiling and giving his all, to be who he was, and to stand firm in his values.

Listening to these stories made me realize his legacy and what he stood for. But that just turned my world upside down. I started having an existential crisis. *What is the meaning of life? What is my purpose? What is my legacy? What is my reason for being on this earth? What would I be remembered for? Would I have made a difference or impact on anyone's life? Why are we here on this earth? Is this what life is all about; going to school, then college, 9 to 5 work, get married, have kids, take care of kids and grandkids and die? There has to be more.*

There is something about being in the presence of someone when they are taking their last breath. Two sacred events can change your life or perspectives forever: Watching a baby come into this world and being in the presence of someone transitioning out of this world. Birth and death are two ends of the spectrum, one thought as a miracle, and the other deemed dark and undesirable. Knowing that as soon as we decide to exist in the womb, we take our first step towards death, our life could be just for few weeks in the womb, a few days on earth or living into our nineties. Our bodies are mortal, borrowed until our purpose is fulfilled. This impermanence is all around us; we are part of nature, and nature constantly shows us evolution, change, and impermanence. We all are interconnected, woven in the framework of the universe, and we are constantly evolving together, collectively following and moving to the rhythm and dance of birth, life, and death.

After my dad's death, we were devastated; we went through a series of traumas, a compilation of changes, leaving us to deal with complicated grief. We all individually grieved, adjusting to the loss, realigning to the empty space of an elder, adjusting to the period of relocations, and maneuvering, readjusting, and restructuring to that void that my dad left in the family. It took a toll physically, mentally, and emotionally on each of us. But as always, life moves on, and you start falling back to the old normal ways. I started going back to work and getting involved in the kids' school, activities, and housework. I was not happy, I couldn't sleep, I was depressed, and affected my health. I was angry all the time.

I bypassed that window of opportunity to change, to evolve, and to think and be different.

Once you send out questions into the universe, there is no turning back. Things were falling apart, and nothing was working out for me. I decided to drop out of my doctorate program and took a bold decision to invest in myself to improve my personal life. I took off on a quest to calm my anger, search for true joy, my purpose, and the meaning of life. The best decision I made was to certify in Reiki (universal life force energy), a Japanese form of touch healing. Everything started falling into its place, and I gave myself the time and space needed to heal, grieve, love, and take care of myself. I saw the ripple effect it caused and was aware of the miracles every moment of life was bringing. I saw the synchronicities and the magic life holds. I saw the love and light that we truly all are.

My experiences set me on a journey to find out all I could about death. I would say there is something about death and me, but I really didn't know what it meant. I read about how we are in a loop of life and death and started looking into Moksha (liberation). I realized that most of us are fearful of death, the unknown, the suffering, and the pain it could bring. Ultimately, we fear being alone in our final moments and living without our loved ones.

Last year, I was intuitively guided to an End-Of-Life Doula course. As an empath, I feel very deeply, and to read, hear, and watch videos of immense grief, loss, pain, and regrets was gut-wrenching. But the numerous stories of individuals close to transition, from seeing the light and/or being surrounded by angels and their loved ones in other realms, was truly hopeful and comforting. I was fascinated and instantly drawn to concepts of Unconditional Positive Regard developed by Carl Rogers, a client-centered therapy, and Dignity Therapy, developed by Dr. Harvey Max Chochinov to assist and relieve psychological and existential distress in patients at the end of life. It was a new trajectory. I was led on a path of deeper knowing, being more present. I cultivated heart listening, a tool that allows me to use all my senses, and a deeper level of communication. I could create a safe, healing space, and it overflowed in my daily interactions.

The course also showed me how my dad's death was the momentum for my legacy, to be on my path, and follow my purpose. In my father's death, I found life, living a life with awareness, and making honest self-choices without regrets. *Why wait till the end of life to think if my life matters or if I have an impact in this world? Will I be honored or remembered?* I pondered often. Talking about life can help the process of accepting death.

Legacy work is a life review, a chance to see the opportunity that exists in every moment to change, to correct the wrongs, and be the love and light we are.

Legacy can be of wealth and properties, values, service, generational history, stories, recipes, food, or heirlooms. And it is our service to those we love, to our family, friends, and community. Through legacy work, there is a chance to uncover what matters most in our personal lives through our experiences and reflections. We discover and share the wisdom, which is most important.

Live a story that lasts an eternity.

Imagine living a life that really matters now. Imagine being remembered long before the end-of-life. Take the opportunity to align with your wisdom, values, and goals proactively.

- It will make better use of your time and resources.
- It will influence your day-to-day decisions in a positive way.
- Gaining clarity can give your life meaning and purpose.
- You show up in the world each day with love, kindness, and compassion.
- You increase your impact by connecting deeply and personally with each individual.
- You live with greater insight, intention, and purpose and create a ripple effect in the world.

THE TOOL

Your legacy project could take any form. Elaborate or simple, all are meaningful. One of the most important things to know about legacy work is that there are no rules, no restrictions, no limitations, and no eligibility criteria. You don't have to have a lot of money or time, and you don't even have to have a terminal diagnosis.

Intentional or not, we all leave behind these pieces of ourselves that others will remember us by. These memories and mementos are our legacies. It's the act of sitting down and taking time to purposefully creating something for the people you love and care about. Remember, it isn't about death and dying; it's about life and living. It's about making connections and sharing precious moments with the special people in your life. It provides a unique opportunity to reflect on your life and process through the events and people who shaped it while still planning for the future. It can be a powerful coping tool not only for you but for the people around you.

Starting the process of legacy work can seem daunting or a little overwhelming. If you're struggling with where to begin or need a little help along the way, reach out at www.hemalivora.com/resources.

Here are some activities that will guide you in creating your legacy.

- A scrapbook with pictures, keepsakes related to a particular time in your life
- A collection of your favorite recipes/food
- A blanket made out of your favorite T-shirts or other fabric items
- A life review worksheet
- A family tree
- Handprints of you and/or your loved ones in plaster
- A video montage of your best honest advice, failures, successes, most cherished memories, or stories about your family history
- Cards written or gifts purchased for a future birthday, holiday, or special occasions
- A letter, poem, or a song created specifically for your loved ones.
- Journal
- Volunteer
- Create family traditions
- Start a leadership or mentoring program
- Start a hobby that you always wanted to but didn't have the time

The focus is to write a letter and to remember it's about living well (up until death), finding meaning, and honoring you and where you are. I hope this helps bring your memories, thoughts, and feelings into perspective. Getting these thoughts on paper really opens your eyes to what you thought was a dull, boring life, and how beautiful it has been, and how much you have accomplished so far. I hope you can be fully open and vulnerable. This is a letter just for you to keep and share with your loved ones. What would you want your loved ones to know and celebrate about you?

Plan for about 60 minutes. Sit comfortably in a quiet place with a pen and a journal. You can meditate or play comforting music.

- Close your eyes and take a few deep breaths.
- Allow yourself to relax and your whole body to melt.

Below are a few questions to ask yourself. You can contemplate and meditate on each question if you like:

- Reflect on your life history, particularly the parts that you remember most. When did you feel most alive?
- What specific things would you want your family to know and remember about you?
- What are the most important roles you have played in life? Why were they so important to you?
- What are your most important accomplishments, and what do you feel most proud of?
- Are there particular things that you feel still need to be said to your loved ones?
- What are your hopes and dreams for your loved ones?
- What have you learned about life, and what advice and guidance would you want to pass along to others?
- Are there words or instructions you would like to offer your family to help prepare them for the future?
- In creating this memento, are there other things that you would like included?
- What are your hopes, dreams, and aspirations?

Take this journey of self-discovery, a blueprint for living and making a difference. Start connecting your life to a bigger story. Live life with intention and purpose. Let your life be your legacy.

Hemali V. Vora, MPT, is a holistic Physical Therapist, MFR Practitioner, Certified Integrative Nutrition Coach, Reiki Master Teacher, and an End of Life Doula. She is an expert holistic practitioner, intuitive energy healer, and spiritual mentor. She skillfully guides clients to their unique legacy blueprint. Hemali helps clients with end of life transitions with ease.

Her purpose in this lifetime is to guide healthcare workers and caregivers towards radical self-care, unconditional self-love, self-compassion, and inner peace. She empowers clients to tap into the powers that lie within, so they can be the love, be the voice, be the ears, and be the strength they seek in others.

Having gone through her own journey filled with weight struggles, health challenges, and healing crises, Hemali has learned the power of intuition and our body's potential to heal itself through nourishing its body, mind, emotion, and spirit. According to her, nutrition, movement, energy, spiritual, and shadow work play a vital role in healing disease, disharmony, pain, overwhelm, burnouts, and traumas.

Over two decades of working in healthcare, she has helped and guided hundreds of patients, clients, and their families with chronic illnesses, disabilities, personal traumas, and in their spiritual journeys. She integrates ancient wisdom and modern science in her work. Hemali offers one-on-one or group sessions in her office, in your home, and online. www.hemalivora.com, www.facebook.com/coachhemali, www.instagram.com/_happy_healthy_u

CHAPTER 21

REAL LIFE TIME TRAVEL

ACCESS PAST & FUTURE SELVES TO SOLVE ANY PROBLEM NOW

ANNE-MARIE HARNETT BS, LMT, RTT

MY STORY

As I sit in my therapist's office, we are making plans for how to save my inner six-year-old. She is in a high level of distress, and the situation she is in is not safe.

My therapist is using a style of therapy called "Internal Family Systems" (IFS), where you access your clear, calm, and compassionate "adult self" to assist in healing internal parts of you, which can be of different ages.

I teach a similar approach, Realizing Your Sublime Energies (RYSE), where you are taught to access your "aligned self" to create healing with your different inner aspects or sub-personalities.

In this situation with my therapist, we decide to send my clear, calm, adult back in time to rescue my inner six-year-old. I request some reinforcements: A female angel, a male angel with a sword, and a winged horse to whisk us out of there.

When we arrive back in time, I start by introducing myself to my inner six-year-old. "Hello, I am you, grown-up." She looks at me, and her eyes grow wide. "We made it? We're an adult now?" Tears start streaming down my face. It had never occurred to me that my frightened, inner children did not know we had survived.

"Yes, we made it. And we're doing really well. Would you like to join me in the future where I will protect you?"

She hesitates. After all, I am a stranger to her. I show her an image of my dog, Bacca, and the beautiful home I have created. She looks on in interest and then is distracted by the powerful energy of the two angels and the flying horse.

"We are here to rescue you," I said. "You don't need to be afraid anymore. I'm so sorry that I didn't come back for you sooner."

She gently pets the horse's velvety nostrils and looks around one last time.

"Are you ready? Is there anything that you want to bring with you?"

She picks up a stuffed animal and nods. I offer my help and secure her on the horse. The angels keep watch as we leap into the air and fly into the present.

THE TOOL

How can your "future self" save you now?

This tool can be used in two different ways: you can go back in time from the present and rescue or assist younger versions of yourself, or you can advance in time and access an older version of yourself who already holds the answers to what you're struggling with now.

This is incredibly powerful work.

And as in my experience above, sometimes we need assistance from others such as angels, guides, animals, superheroes, any beings you find supportive, safe, and powerful. But you don't need to do this work on your own. If there is significant trauma in your past, you may want to invite in the help of a trained professional.

1. GOING BACK IN TIME

A. Take out a journal or something to write on. Sometimes multi-colored pens, markers, or crayons are helpful.

B. Sit somewhere comfortable, close your eyes, and take a few deeper breaths without forcing them. I like to put a hand on my lower belly when I want to connect with younger ages and be present in my body. The second chakra, which is below the belly button, reflexes to ages 0-5 years. The third chakra reflexes to ages 6-11 years, so place a hand right below your diaphragm—the "upside-down V" at the front of your body under your ribs—if you want to connect with those ages instead.

C. Begin by calling in your clear, calm, compassionate, centered adult self to ground you and support you during this work. Breathe into your most centered self. Take a moment and write down what it feels like to connect with that place in you.

D. Once you feel centered, ask to connect with a young age from your past that needs help. Since this work can bring up big feelings, make sure that you feel safe and supported in the present moment.

   If the younger you is in an unsafe situation, it is best to remove them and bring them forward to a safe time and space. You will construct the safe space with your younger ones later in step L.

   If the younger you needs more support and love, you and the beings that you bring with you can facilitate that connection. The work that follows is specifically for the rescue of an inner child from a dangerous environment. And you define what dangerous is for you.

E. As you get a sense of an age, write down what you are seeing, feeling, and noticing. What is the younger you wearing? Where is she/he? Any information that comes through is helpful. Simple words and phrases are often the best. Write it all down.

F. Now, call in the beings of love and light that you would like to help you connect with your younger self.

   Examples:

   1. Female or male angels: love, softness, safety, protection.
   2. Guides: calm and wise.

3. Young animals like puppies or bunnies can help a child to relax and smile.
4. Older, bigger animals like horses, dogs, and big cats can bring a sense of safety and protection.
5. Superheroes who have powers that are helpful in the situation that you are facing and whom your inner child connects with.

You want to pick just a few helpers so that your inner child doesn't feel overwhelmed.

G. Write down who you will be bringing with you. And call forth (out loud is best) your "calm, clear, compassionate, centered adult self" and the "beings of love, light, and protection" you have invited in to make this journey back through time on this rescue mission.

H. Either close your eyes and imagine going back through time to where your little one is in distress or write out the story in your journal, allowing the details to come through you. Keep breathing and relaxing your body.

I. Once back in time, introduce yourself to your young one. Tell them some things about you that might be reassuring. Write out the dialogue if that is helpful. You can use the writing from your non-dominate hand to represent your younger self.

J. Introduce your younger self to whomever you have brought with you; angels, animals, superheroes. Give them a moment to connect. Write a description of the connections that occur.

   Then ask if your young one wants to leave where they are and come with you to a safe place in the future. Project an image to them of what that future place looks like. Allow your younger self the space to decide "yes" or "no." She/He may need to get to know you better first.

K. If she/he is ready, invite your younger self to step into a magical way of travel that you have created and come back with you so that they can now be safe.

   If she/he needs more time, create a date and time when you will come back. **Keep that promise. Write in your journal when you will do this exercise again and reconnect with your young, distressed one.

L. Once she/he is back with you, work to create a safe space for your little one to reside. It could be in your heart or a landscape of your imagining; a treehouse, cabin, Victorian house, home by the water, or in the mountains. Create a space with food, light, games, playmates, animals, angels, and safety. Write out a description of this safe space, this new home for your inner little ones, that you are co-creating with them. You can make changes at any time.

   Example: inner children dwelling in a large Victorian next to a beach. The house is full of books, games, and clothes to play dress up. Angels reside to rock and sing to the little ones. A table is laden with all manner of cakes, cookies, fruit, and other delicious food; there are no restrictions. A side yard beckons with trees to climb and swings to ride. Big cats and angels with swords walk the perimeter to keep all safe.

Below is the second approach to using your future self to help you now.

2. GOING FORWARD IN TIME

A. Take out a journal or something to write on. Sometimes multi-colored pens, markers, or crayons are helpful.

B. Sit somewhere comfortable, close your eyes, and take a few deeper breaths without forcing them. I like to put a hand on my heart to connect to my emotions and my body.

C. Call upon your clear, calm, compassionate, centered adult self to assist with this work. It's always a good idea to hook into your places of strength when doing inner work.

D. Connect to the problem that you are trying to solve, the place where you feel stuck. Write it down.

E. Now ask to connect with your future self who has already solved the problem. Or the time where the solution has shown itself. Call forth the future age when this issue is resolved. Maybe you want to connect with the time when your life partner shows up or when you are out of physical pain. You might need to go forward one year, five years, or more.

F. Ask your future self to describe to you what the solution feels like. What does it feel like to have found your life partner or be out of pain? Write down whatever words or phrases come to you. Don't edit. Use all of your senses to feel into this future time. What do things look like, sound like, smell like, and feel like?

G. Now, thank your future self and imagine merging with the solution and feeling the feelings of completion, ease, and joy. Feel it happening now.

H. Write down anything else that you notice or want to remember.

I. Take some slow, deep breaths and come fully back into the present moment.

You may need to connect to your future self who has the solution that you are seeking more than once to really get it into your body and being now. The more relaxed you can get, the more the information will flow. Maybe play some relaxing music when doing these exercises.

Check out my resource link to see and hear me walk you through this process. Doing this as a guided meditation can be powerfully useful.

HarnettHealing.com/UltimateGuideResources

Connect to and enjoy the wisdom that lives inside you. You can heal yourself. And I'm here if you'd like some additional support.

I started my career in health and wellness with a Bachelor of Science degree in Cellular and Molecular Biology from Tulane University. I then went to massage school for fun and fell in love with it. I specialized in pre and post-natal massage and labor & delivery support for three years. I then went on to become a massage and Polarity instructor at the Massachusetts-based company Spa Tech. I taught massage, Polarity therapy, anatomy, ethics, and RYSE. I am one of six people in the world who is a certified RYSE Teacher Trainer. RYSE teaches people how to clear and repair their own energy systems and gives them the freedom to take back their lives. I love to teach RYSE and watch people reclaim their power and health!

I have been working with clients in my private massage and energy work practice, Harnett Healing, for twenty-three years. I work with clients in person and by phone. Using sound, crystals, light touch, and deep touch, I re-balance your system on all levels. I look for the source of your suffering, clearing past lives, and healing inner children. Together, we evolve your system into the best version of yourself. I say 'we' because I don't do this work alone. I have much support and guidance from the other dimensions. I work with what I call my "energetic posse," and you have one too.

Loving all things healing and high frequency, I also work with certified pure, therapeutic-grade essential oils. They assist in balancing us mentally, physically, and emotionally while assisting healing on a cellular level.

I also utilize a state-of-the-art frequency device from Germany called a Healy. It will scan you and tell you what is out of balance. We have found it to be amazingly accurate. And then it sends frequencies to you to bring you back into homeostasis. It is FDA cleared for treating pain and is a class two medical device. It works in person and over the phone.

I've done many advanced trainings through the years: Cranial therapy (four levels), visceral manipulation, strain counter-strain, neuromuscular therapy, trigger point release, integrative manual therapy, Matrix Energetics, sacred geometry, and much more. I have also completed the level one training in Internal Family Systems. IFS combined with RYSE, creates a powerful synergy that catapults my inner child work to a place of empowered, client-centric healing. You learn how to heal yourself with my support and guidance.

Having written a chapter for the best-selling book, *The Ultimate Guide to Self-Healing Volume 3*, I am thrilled to be contributing to Volume 4. Enjoy all of these fabulous tips to healing yourself and stay connected to this amazing community of healers and teachers.

I look forward to connecting with you and learning how I can support you on your healing journey.

Heart and health.

HarnettHealing.com/UltimteGuideResources

CHAPTER 22

WEALTH CONSCIOUSNESS

PRACTICING PRESENCE IN YOUR MONEY STORY

VERONICA B. LIGHT

This body is not me, but mine. These thoughts are not me, but mine. As I heard these words, I allowed them to permeate through my consciousness while meditating. Feeling a warmth in my heart, I sensed my soul calling me.

The following day, I felt guided to begin practicing conscious presence. This challenge would reveal my limiting beliefs waiting to be transmuted in the light, forgiven and loved by the I that I AM, the I AM presence that resides in the space between thought and form.

Practicing conscious presence would be the platform I used and the gateway towards transforming the limiting beliefs that came up for me over the next 30 days. During that time, I received more and more guidance from my higher self on how to transform them. I experimented with different ideas, techniques, and modalities that included Neuro-Linguistic Programming (NLP), DNA Cell(f) activation, and cognitive science.

After consistently practicing this process, I noticed I wasn't getting triggered like I used to. Instead, I was seeing situations, things, and people from an elevated perspective. I saw how people and situations were helping me solve the puzzle, so to speak. I found myself having more faith and trust in the flow of life.

The I AM presence exists in pure consciousness
and is the bridge between the spiritual and material world.
In this presence, there is stillness, wholeness... Oneness.

~ Veronica B. Light

We know thoughts create emotions, and emotions create our personal reality. When we master our emotions and our thoughts (*heart and brain coherence*), we attract more health and well being, joy, prosperity, peace, abundance, and love for life. This is wealth consciousness. It makes sense, then, that the limiting beliefs we have about money can cut off the circulation from receiving more abundance and wealth in our lives.

To have wealth consciousness, we must create our life consciously, with the best of intentions, for the highest good of all concerned. We know that the people we attract are there because we have drawn them there, and how we *choose* to respond to them and our experiences is shaping our future. Our daily interactions can either come from the ego, the higher mind, or the subconscious mind and can be reactive from the body pain, which can be a way of unconscious self-sabotaging. Triggers show up for us to bring awareness of our limiting beliefs so we can take responsibility for transforming them to the best of our ability from where we are right now.

Wealth consciousness *isn't* about how much money you have. Some people have millions of dollars in the bank and lose sleep at night over the fear of losing their assets, which is *not* emotionally healthy. Therefore that person is not tuned-in to wealth consciousness despite how it might seem in the material world.

Wealth consciousness is about having the inner knowing that lack is an illusion of separation and wealth and abundance is something that we are. With the practice of conscious presence, we can transform our lives and contribute to the evolution of consciousness itself, *the ripple effect.* The more people that practice conscious presence and transform limiting beliefs, the more we contribute to elevating the collective consciousness to a more harmonious state of *Being.*

My continued practice of conscious presence has evolved over the years and has proven to be my greatest teacher. This practice has gifted me with a deeper sense of purpose, and I continue to reach new levels of consciousness, which is priceless.

MY STORY

I can still recall the scent of cocoa that stimulated my senses as I carefully sipped a cup of hot chocolate with almond milk that elegantly washed down a slice of one of my favorite desserts; vegan, flourless chocolate cake. *Yum!* I was sitting outside of a quaint café in Little Italy with my friend and colleague, Sara. It was a few years ago, back when I was still married to John. Sara and I used to meet there once a week to catch up and exchange ideas.

After an hour-long conversation, there was a short pause. Sara looked over at me and said, "Veronica, you went through a spiritual awakening; you know your life is going to change, right?" It was confirmation of what I sensed as well—*deep breath.* "I've been feeling the call to pursue my true vocation," I nodded. As Sara smiled at this idea and nodded with approval, the waiter handed us the check, and we concluded our visit.

On my drive back home, I felt *the nudge* again, the nudge to dissolve my brokerage business. *Gulp!* I say *my* because I started it and ran it all on my own. *John would not like this!* My throat felt tight at the mere thought of sharing this idea with him.

John had been out of commission due to health issues, and I was the sole breadwinner for years and wasn't really sure if he was even ready to go back to work. *What to do, what to do? Ugh. Deep breath.* I would sit with this idea and go within for guidance on this life-changing decision.

That evening, as I walked into our meditation room, I went straight to my prayer altar. There, I lit a white, lavender-scented candle, anointed my hands with lavender essential oil, set an intention, and told myself; *Thy will be done.*

Sitting lotus style on my square, pink Moroccan style meditation cushion, I took a few deep breaths and began to relax. *Ahhhh.* A few minutes in, my brain waves were in a theta state, and I felt connected to my higher self. I sat there in silence for a while longer. *If it's in the highest good of all to dissolve my brokerage business, please send me a clear sign,* I requested. Closing with a gratitude prayer, I would leave it in God's hands.

I spent the next several weeks practicing conscious presence, and it was no surprise when the limiting beliefs about money began to surface at the thought of taking a leap of faith to follow my calling. As I brought awareness to those beliefs, I began to work on transforming them according to my guidance that consisted of using different techniques. The more I worked on clearing and shifting those limiting beliefs, the lighter I felt with what were once heavy thoughts.

It was a typical busy workday in my home office. I had been working since 6 am, and after a late lunch, John and I took our dog for a walk. The weather was perfect with a slight breeze, and John seemed to be in good spirits. We ran into our neighbors during our walk, an older couple (Diane and Jack) who lived in our cul-de-sac. "Looking good there, John!" said Jack. "Oh, thanks!" John said with a smile on his face. "Yes, he does look like he's feeling better from his surgery!" nodded Diane. We all smiled, and John chuckled with gratitude. "That's great! Are you back to work yet?" asked Jack. "Oh, umm…not quite there yet, but hopefully soon," John said while placing both his hands over his body pain that was in the solar plexus area. After a brief pause and change of subject, we said so long and continued our walk with the dog. John seemed deep in thought, and we walked in silence for a while. I was thinking, *wow! The sign I asked for is coming—deep breath. Don't attach to an outcome;* I reminded myself.

When we got back home from our walk, John went into the kitchen with the dog, and I went back to the home office to check-in and follow up on the clients in my pipeline. A couple of hours later, I went upstairs and felt called to sit down and do a meditation to connect with my higher self. I didn't go to the meditation room, however. I sat down lotus style on a sofa chair in our master bedroom. Somewhere between getting comfortable and before closing my eyes, something very interesting happened.

Out of nowhere, I saw an image about a foot long and wide and about two feet from my third eye. It was as if the image was being projected out in the physical world through my third eye. The image wasn't still. It was moving fast as if it was going through a tunnel. It reached the end of the tunnel, and there I saw several images that flashed in front of me very clear and fast! The images were related to my business; the articles of corporation, the page with my signature and the name of my business, the business checkbook, and all the paperwork attached to the business. Then, I saw the tunnel again. It was going fast and went into what looked like a beautifully landscaped park filled with a bounty of lovely flowers and beautiful trees. The image zoomed in closer, and there I saw a tombstone that said *RIP.* It was where all the images were placed, and I heard a thump that sounded like a door closing. The image was gone. *Whoa!* I felt the thump in my heart. I was taken aback by the experience. My heart was racing, and I sat there, processing what happened. *Wow! Deep breath.* Placing my right hand on the center of my chest, I breathed slowly and deeply for a few minutes. It was miraculously profound. It was clear, as requested. I was humbled.

The following morning, I woke up feeling accomplished as I looked over to my left and saw John sound asleep. I took a moment to go within, and I was reminded how far I had come with transforming my limiting beliefs about money. The emotions that once held me back were transformed. I was feeling lighter and empowered to tell John my plan to dissolve my brokerage business and move forward with starting a soul-based business.

Later that day, I told John how I felt, what I desired, my plan on pursuing my true vocation, and my thoughts about dissolving my brokerage business. He was very upset and proceeded to raise his voice as he gave me his two cents and then gave me the silent treatment. A couple of days later, he came to terms with this idea and asked me to help him with his resume. *Wow!* These words were like music to my ears, and frankly, I wasn't sure I would ever hear them. I was experiencing miracles.

The fear I had letting go of what was no longer serving the highest good transmuted and gave me the confidence to move forward with following my true vocation and living a fulfilling life. New doors and opportunities began to open that wouldn't have otherwise, and I felt more love for life than ever before pursuing my passion and dreams.

When we are in a wealth consciousness mindset, we recognize the fear of uncertainty and don't allow it to dwell in our consciousness. Instead, we remember that dwelling in fear is what creates the limiting belief in the first place.

- Veronica B. Light

THE TOOL

The first step towards a wealth consciousness mindset is being honest with yourself about your current money story. The following is an exercise to assist you in bringing awareness to your limiting beliefs:

- Find some time for yourself and set up a sacred space where you won't be interrupted for about 15-20 minutes with a paper and pen or a computer by your side.
- Get comfortable in a seated position (not too comfortable that you doze off).
- Set the intention that you would like to connect with your limiting beliefs about money and abundance.
- Close your eyes, take a few, long deep breaths until you feel like you are relaxed.
- Focus on your breath and allow it to flow naturally.
- Once you feel yourself going into a deeper relaxation in a theta state, ask your higher self to reveal to you your limiting beliefs about money.
- Continue to focus on your breath and allow the words, thoughts, ideas, and memories from childhood and adulthood about money to come to the surface.
- When you feel that the information you were ready to receive about your money story is complete, conclude your meditation practice.
- Write down any thoughts, ideas, and memories that come to mind.
- Write your money story based on those limiting beliefs.

Your money story can be used as the catalyst to shift your beliefs towards wealth consciousness to welcome more abundance and prosperity in your life.

You are invited to join the next online
Wealth Consciousness Challenge
Change your Money Story Course

You are only a shift in perception away from having more prosperity, wealth, and abundance.

www.veronicablight.com/resources

The Wealth Consciousness Challenge is about practicing expanded awareness of the life you have created, looking at it without judgment, forgiving yourself, and shifting your limiting beliefs to experience better mental and emotional health, which is key to living a prosperous, abundant, fulfilling life.

- Clear the energy around your money story.
- Shift your limiting beliefs around money.
- Re-write your money story from a heart and soul-centered space.
- Learn practices that will support you in shifting your consciousness.
- Learn techniques on how to elevate your vibrational frequency.
- Receive guided meditations to deepen your connection to your highest self for inner guidance.
- Learn techniques on how to practice expanded awareness in your money story.
- Learn how to practice conscious presence.
- Feel empowered in your new money story.

Veronica B. Light, International Bestselling Author

Veronica specializes in conscious leadership development. Her experience as a transformation coach and holistic practitioner for over a decade has earned her a unique approach to shifting limiting beliefs that powerfully supports people on their path to self-actualization.

Let's connect:

https://linktr.ee/veronicabthelight

www.veronicablight.com

CHAPTER 23

COMMUNION WITH SPACES

A BOSS LADY'S GUIDE TO A HAPPY, HEALTHY HOME

EKTAA RAJANI

MY STORY

Forty kilometers outside Bangalore, India, in a small town called Devanahalli, my family owns a 20-acre farmhouse. I have many fond childhood memories of the place. My sister and I played with rabbits and chicken, climbed trees, plucked sapotas, mangoes, and tamarind, bathed under the swimming pool waterfall, swam with the ducks in the pond, and sat in our parents' laps in a two-seater swan paddle boat; we took in the view of the one-acre artificial lake and enjoyed every small pleasure that a life away from the city could offer. Over the years, we got busy with school and couldn't visit the farmhouse as much as we would have liked. The lush green trees, vibrant flowers and fruits, and inherent joy of the land seemed to fade with the echoes of our laughter.

My family had a strong desire to revive the beautiful energies of the land, and it had been my father's dream to build a temple. In 2014, I enrolled for a Bachelor's degree in Vaastu that started me off on a journey into the depths of this 3000-year-old science used to construct temples, forts, monuments, cities, and homes. Four months into the program, I was equipped with the knowledge to bring my father's dream to fruition. I made over 100 trips to oversee the construction of my family temple, and I vividly remember the trip I made on my temple's first anniversary. On my way, the weather turned as I drove past the International Airport. Upon entering Devanahalli, I drove down the winding roads for two kilometers before getting off the state highway to enter my farmhouse. The line of mango trees covered the temple from direct view at the gate, and when I caught a glimpse of it halfway down the muddy road, it was love at first sight all over again!

I lifted the makeshift wooden gate that sat in the grooves of the double-layered stone compound wall, set it aside next to the holy basil plant by the entrance, took off my shoes, and looked up, my heart full of love and adoration for this magnificent being. The temple stood 10-feet tall on a raised stone foundation, grey walls with four golden pillars adorning each side, and the terracotta tiled roof ended in a copper Kalash that shone brightly against the overcast skies. The granite floor was still warm from the morning sun, and the familiar smell of mangoes and rain was in the air. Placing my hand on the outside wall, I circumambulated the six-foot by six-foot structure, soaking in the little details: the trim detailing on the hip rafters, a swastika etched on the back window, brass fixtures, and inverted lotus carvings on the front doors that held behind them space as potent as a 100-year-old temple. Propping myself on the north compound wall under the mango trees, I thought back to the moment I started to understand the mysteries of Vaastu.

Tears rolling down my cheeks, face buried between my knees, the desire to build a family temple was strong, but the responsibility to bring it to life was wearing me down. Sitting by the dried-up artificial lake in the afternoon heat, I felt like a total failure. My Vaastu classmates and I worked tirelessly for the past two days, searching for an ideal spot for the temple close to the mango trees. We dug in three places and unearthed an ant's nest, a sewage pipe, and roots, none suitable to have in a temple foundation. The next day was an auspicious day to begin construction, and we were running out of time. *Why did you agree to do this? You are going to let your family down.* The voice in my head was all-consuming. I looked up to see my classmates sitting on the other side of the lake, animated in conversation, unaware of my state of mind. In an attempt to fight off the negative thoughts, I closed my eyes, taking in the cool breeze against my face, the rustling of the leaves of the silver oak trees that sounded like waves crashing on the beach, distant sounds of aircraft taking off, and the warmth of the soil. Each muscle in my body slowly started to relax, the stress melted, and every passing moment created a deeper connection to my surroundings. A tiny whisper, clear against my quiet mind, rose from within. *Ask for guidance.* I took a couple of deep breaths waiting for more. None came. Addressing the land, my late grandfather, who worked tirelessly on this property, and my inner being, I said out loud, "Please guide and support me in constructing this temple." A wave of relief swept all over my body as I soaked in the energies from my environment. When my body brought me out of the trance-like state, I opened my eyes, and although only a few minutes had passed, everything seemed new!

Guided by my body, I walked back to the site with a tingling sensation all over and a familiar sense of knowing what needed to be done. My classmates already made their way back and were busy working when I stood five feet west from our previous digs and declared, "This is the perfect spot!" The words flew out of my mouth before I could catch them. *Is this my body's way of telling me what my inner being already knows?* With nothing to lose, my classmates and I pulled out our tapes and started measuring out from that point; no trees in the diagonals or in the path of the front door and back window, enough space to accommodate the compound wall, and no roots, ant's nest, or pipe upon digging. I could hardly believe it; it was the perfect spot! The forces of the universe seemed to come together, working with me to birth this potent space.

Ever since the incident by the lake, my inner being became my compass, my guiding force. The more I relied on it, the easier things became. Temple construction entails a lot of precision, use of sacred mathematics, and measures requiring us to be accurate to 1/64th of an inch (the thickness of a strand of hair). On one particular occasion, I had to ensure the center of the roof was aligned to the center of the floor before fixing it into position. Sitting on my heels, bent over, tape in hand while a classmate stood on a ladder with a plumb bob dropped from the roof, I called out instructions. After the first ten minutes, the numbers got blurry, my hands stiff, and I started feeling lightheaded. Closing my eyes, I centered myself, took in the space around me, and handed over control to my body. In 20 minutes, we had the roof locked into position.

As construction went on, I found myself connecting to the temple with greater ease. It would paint me an image of the blank spaces, guide me on the next steps, or draw me to a space that needed attention every time I asked, "How do you desire to look and feel in this world?" A stone fence, granite flooring for the compound, and a longer entrance in the west to accommodate a temple tree were a few of its strong desires. This communion and sense of co-creation with my temple made me feel like a child, searching for answers in the gentle whispers, nudges, and signs. When we finally completed construction, I was beaming with pride, not because I poured my heart and soul into this project but because it taught me how to sensitize myself to energies of space and trust my inner being. Vaastu being the alignment of body, energies, and space, set me on the path of understanding how to leverage this alignment. It would shape my soul in ways that would unfold in the years to come.

Fast forward to the year 2020. I live in a palatial apartment with my in-laws and husband in the home of Bollywood, Mumbai. Although it had been over a year since our wedding, I still felt like a guest in my husband's home. Apart from a few things from my home in Bangalore, this space never felt like mine. I was yearning to belong, be owned by the space, and most of all, feel at home. On 25 March 2020, when India went into lockdown for nearly three months, the overwhelming feeling of caring for a house that never felt mine left me feeling uneasy and stressed. Although I am an indoor person, being stuck in a home that didn't feel like one and not having an option to step out, feel the earth, and expanse of the universe affected my mind, body, and soul. None of the modalities I learned over the years—Reiki, Access Consciousness, and Body Whispering—seemed to create enough change for me. I needed more.

Sometime in October, I came across a video on Feng Shui, a Chinese practice, whose origins can be traced back to Vaastu. It instantly reminded me of my temple days. Without wasting a minute, I jumped onto the bright orange lounge chair in my room and made myself comfortable. I took a couple of deep breaths and stared at the clock placed on the wall in front of me. Seeing the colorful paintings of birds, leaves, and flowers on it was always a delight. Ever since the day I bought and placed it on the empty wall to the right of the television, the room felt a little more mine. Sitting with that feeling, I closed my eyes, taking in the sounds of the wind whistling through the slightly open window. I heard the birds chirping and ticking of the clock and allowed the space outside me to enter my body through my senses, creating a movement of energies within. There was a sudden surge of thoughts, and although unnerving, I didn't resist them. In my mind's eye, I saw my room and a dark cloud covering the cupboard filled with books that was close to my side of the bed. I felt restless and a sudden urge to change the energy of that space.

Letting my body guide me through this process, I leaped off the chair and headed over to the cupboard that was tightly packed with books from floor to ceiling. Sliding the door open, staring at the shelves, I was filled with rage at how I accommodated my books in empty spaces so as not to disturb my husband's book arrangement. *I live on the outskirts of my room. No wonder I feel like a guest!* My breath became hot and heavy. Desperately trying not to scream, I grabbed a couple of books and threw them onto the ground. Thud! Thud! Books were flying everywhere; onto the floor, bed, and bedside table. I kept going until I had emptied all shelves of my husband's books. I gathered my books and arranged them on a waist-high shelf. Having a shelf dedicated all to me felt so expansive! The feeling of being crushed to fit in small spaces, contracted and mangled, eased up as I stared at the empty shelves above and below mine.

How many women do I know who this to themselves? Compromising, adjusting, making themselves small enough to fit into other's lives. Are they even aware of it? Or worse, they know and continue to diminish themselves, convincing themselves of a day where they would have all the space in the world to be their true self? I have been doing this to myself in my own home, assuming the world outside me was to blame! These thoughts made my head hurt. I picked up the books from the floor and arranged them in the empty shelves, realizing that I had to create space for me being me, no matter how overwhelming it was for those around me. To keep the momentum going, I repeated this exercise in the study, living room, and kitchen, claiming and owning space that was rightfully mine. A sense of belonging started to seep in, and walking through my home never felt better.

The full realization of communion with the spaces around me occurred when I started acknowledging all my experiences. After that fortunate day in October, there was a deeper unfolding of the meaning of Vaastu and space. The word space has come to mean many things to me: space you hold for someone to share their thoughts, feelings, and emotions without judgement, space you hold with your inner being, the physical spaces we occupy, and space we hold with our lives, body, relationships, work, and the universe. Through communion with physical, emotional, mental, and spiritual spaces, my relationships have improved, and I am happier and more present in my life.

THE TOOL

VAASTU EXERCISE

What you'll need to do before you begin: Walk around your home, spending a few minutes in each space. Identify a room or space that is inviting, or you enjoy spending time in.

What to keep in mind: Trust your body, inner being, and your home to guide you through this process. This is a simple mediation and can be done anywhere, at any time. There is no right or wrong in this process, so try to enjoy it at much as you can.

Exercise: Set aside at least 20 minutes for this exercise. You can find the audio version of the meditation on my website – https://www.ektaarajani.com/resources

Find a comfortable spot and sit with your feet touching the ground or lie down on your back. Close your eyes and take a couple of deep breaths. Relax your jaws, neck, shoulder, back, and legs. Relax your feet, knees, hips, chest, and forehead. Connect to the energies of your body and observe the areas where you feel any tightness. Placing your attention there, take a few deep breaths until you feel it melt away. As your body starts to relax and open up, feel the cosmic energies flow from the top of your head down to the tips of your toes. Simultaneously, feel the energies of the earth rise through your feet into your body and out your crown chakra. Allow yourself to be a channel of these two healing energies. If you feel any resistance coming up, don't fight it. Trust your body to allow space for this experience.

Feel the energies in and around your body. Visualizing them as a ball of white light, slowly expand it out in all directions, two feet, four feet, until you fill in the corners of the room. Soak in the space around you; the sounds, smells, visuals, sensations, colors, and memories. What emotions does it evoke within you? How do you feel about this space? What is the quality of the thoughts you're experiencing? Allow them to flow naturally and ensure you are kind to yourself during this process.

Slowly expand out into the living, dining, kitchen, bathroom, and all the other rooms, one-by-one, till you fill in the corners of your home. Ensure your home or apartment is encompassed by this ball of light. Take as much time as you require to get to this space. Look at your home from above, observe how you feel. Give your home a big hug, shower it with good feelings and mention all the things you truly appreciate about it.

Visualize yourself standing at the front door and pull energy from the universe through your body and guide it into your home. Watch these energies make their way from the front door into every corner and out the back. Keep flowing energy this way till you feel your home has gotten lighter, brighter, or happier. Once you feel lighter, set the intention of how you would like to feel in this space. Saying it out loud helps sometimes. You may experience the contrast of your desires against the prevailing energies, don't let it stop you from asking anyway.

Sense a child-like joy run through your body as you open the front door and enter your home. As you move from one room to another in your mind's eye, sense the expanded energies you've invited into each space. Once you've completed this, ask your body to guide and help create the change you desire and stay open to receiving guidance from the space around you. Request energetic contributions from your inner being, home, the earth, and the cosmos. Trust that every action taken to change the energies will emerge from this space. Spend as much time as you need here.

Open your eyes, look around, and take in the space for a few minutes. Does anything feel different? When you're ready, walk around allowing your body or the space to guide you without controlling any impulses or reactions that you may experience during this process. If you don't know where to begin, moving a few things around, or making small changes in the space might get you started. Sometimes I find stepping away from the space and coming back to it later helps to deal with the overwhelming feelings, and other times, it can lead you to another space that requires attention. Refrain from judging yourself if things don't work out the way you expected them to; know that the space held within your body will call upon you to take action to be in alignment with the space outside you. If you're patient, it will unfold in front of your eyes for you to see.

Through sensitizing ourselves to receiving and understanding the vibrational information of our space, and setting the tone of the vibrations we desire and aligning to them, we can truly start to savor the benefits a home has to offer us and our families.

Ektaa Rajani is an Intuitive Vaastu expert currently residing in Mumbai, India, and is dedicated to co-creating prosperous homes, offices, and digital spaces. With over six years of experience, in addition to providing Vaastu consultation for land, homes, and temple projects, Ektaa also conducts group workshops with easy remedies to heal spaces. She has completed a Bachelor's degree in Vaastu from the American University of Mayonic Science and Technology, USA, and has assisted in the design and construction of four temples in India and one in Portugal. Through intuitive Vaastu, she aims to guide people to overcome obstacles, find balance, and experience communion with their spaces through simple daily practices.

A graphic designer by profession and healer at heart, Ektaa has been learning and practicing various healing modalities from the age of sixteen. Reiki, Access Consciousness, and Body Whispering are a few that have been checked off her long list. As a designer, she has the distinctive ability to understand the energies of her clients and their requirements, seamlessly translating them into designs for digital spaces. You can connect with her at www.ektaarajani.com or mail her at ektaa.rajani@gmail.com

When she isn't busy designing, learning a new modality, or attending the millionth self-healing workshop, you will find Ektaa practicing belly dance moves, binge-watching k-dramas, baking cakes, and chatting away for hours about her life's latest learning to her parents and sister.

CHAPTER 24

PURSUING PLEASURE

THE TRANSFORMATIVE JUSTICE OF FEELING GOOD

STACEY HERRERA

MY STORY

I was 17 when I entered my first long-term relationship. We were young and dramatic, full of passion and brimming with desire, taking advantage of every opportunity to have hormonally-driven, lust-filled, hungry sex.

We had sex when we were happy and when we were upset; with ourselves and each other. We did it during all four seasons, on moonlit nights and bright sunny afternoons. Neither of us cared about the conditions or whether we were physically comfortable.

For us, sex was primal and urgent. It was compulsive and had almost nothing to do with love. We were ignorant and completely oblivious to the fact that we were merely puppets of biology.

That relationship eventually ended, and I began to have sex for different reasons. My 20-something self was in search of love and romance. And as luck would have it, I happened upon a charming tuxedo salesman who fit the bill.

Our sex life was fueled by desire and deep affection. We were smitten, and sex was one of the ways that we expressed our love. He was a patient lover who never rushed. With him, sex was a marathon and not a sprint. And I was so in love that I couldn't see for looking.

I idealized our relationship, believing he was my perfect match and that we'd live happily ever after. And we were good togetheruntil we weren't.

When that relationship ended, I went on a fuck-spree. It was all about proving to myself that I was still marketable, at first. But I soon realized I was sampling, like a foodie traveling to a new land, dizzied by the fragrance of skin I'd never smelled and the taste of mouths I hadn't kissed.

I explored the possibilities through one-night stands and realized that the third time was not always the charm. It was nice to be unattached and unencumbered, with no qualms about whether he would call or whether I would answer if he did. I enjoyed all there was to enjoy and learned that experience really is a good teacher.

By the time I entered my 30s, I was ready for something else. The 30s is what I now call "the decade of self-discovery." I worked hard, played harder, and had a lot of sex with myself. I dedicated entire days to self-pleasure. I called in sick and scheduled vacation days—for no other reason than to feel good.

I taught myself how to be multi-orgasmic and indulged in the fine art of edging. I fucked myself into oblivion on many an occasion, only to wake from slumber and do it all again.

Permitting myself to indulge in carnal delight was liberating, but it was also revolutionary. It changed the way I saw and experienced myself and the way I moved through the world.

Being well-fucked by me boosted my confidence and widened my hips. It straightened my posture and added to my *un-fuck-with-able-ness.* Before then, I thought being a well-fucked woman required a partner, but I was wrong.

Solo sex is sex. Pleasuring myself is how I shed the shame of living in a voluptuous body. Watching me touching me gave my vanity new purpose. I no longer looked at myself to pick me apart. Instead, I admired the woman who stared back at me. I marveled at her almond-shaped eyes and gorgeous grin. Masturbation was an intimate introduction to my muchness.

By the time I turned 40, I was more of myself than I'd ever been, and I was also back on the meat. And by meat, I mean penis. Not that I ever stopped indulging in penile delights, but because I was now so familiar with my own body, penis-in-vagina sex (PIV) was an entirely different experience.

For the record, penetration is only one kind of sex. And although I am not bi-sexual (yet), I believe that sex between all bodies and all genders is valid and magically delicious.

Developing a close relationship with my own body gave me a new appreciation for the human form in its many colors, shapes, and sizes. All bodies are working miracles. I am constantly amazed by the fact that they are capable of creating and experiencing pleasure. And sex is one of the simplest ways to indulge.

Even more than that, sexual pleasure is transformative. Not just in the sense that doing so perpetuates life, but because feeling good changes everything. And by everything, I mean *EVERYTHING.*

PLEASURE IS THE INCARNATION OF POWER.

There is nothing more powerful than the experience of pleasure, sexual and otherwise. Pleasure is the intersection of freedom and peace. It's indulgent and naughty. Self-centric and generous. Intoxicating and contagious.

Pleasure is powerful—and that's why it's so scary.

Indulging desire may seem frivolous, but only because we've been conditioned to believe that we don't deserve it. But we are indeed spirits having a human experience. And pleasure is a necessity, not an option.

It's a primal need.

We try to rise above our animal nature, denying our humanity rather than enhancing it. While we have and continue to evolve, we are still and always will be animals; animals with brains so large that we can override our biology, often to our detriment.

Resisting pleasure is arguably one of the fatal forms of self-harm. And yielding to it is transformative justice.

Transformative justice is about healing the cause rather than punishing the behavior. With that in mind, when you unearth the source of your pain, you can use that knowledge to create new pathways through feeling good.

Your personal brand of justice may be vanilla or kinky. It could be submissive or dominant. Perhaps it's tantric or acrobatic. And to that I say—do you. As long as you indulge with consent and without harm or malice, have at it.

And if you're ready to lean in and pursue sexual pleasure with reckless abandon, I want to help you get to the promised land.

I've taken the liberty of sharing five easy-ish steps to get you started.

THE TOOL

1. BE CURIOUS

Curiosity has been the guiding principle throughout my sexual exploration. Even now that I'm nearing half a century, I'm still curious about my body's ever-changing landscape. And this is a personal invitation for you to stay in a constant state of intrigue.

Look at yourself in the mirror, not to judge, but to see, every single day. Notice things you did not notice before: the laugh lines and the crows' feet. Pay attention to the curl of your toes and the breadth of your chest. Be exceptionally nosey with your genitals. Look at the folds of your labia and the bend of your penis. Taste your essence and tickle your fancy.

Taking an active interest in yourself is self-care. But don't just do it to be healthy—do it to feel good.

Approach every sexual experience with a beginner's mind (even when you're having sex with you)—act brand new—every time. Let go of everything you think you know, and let inquisitiveness be your guide.

Intimacy in and of itself is limitless. It is impossible to know everything there is to know about someone or something. So remaining in a constant state of inquiry with lovers, friends, family, and strangers is to be in a constant state of awe. There is no risk of boredom or obligation when you commit to the process of endless discovery.

2. TALK ABOUT SEX–OFTEN

One of the best ways to get better at sex is to talk about it. Now, this might be a tall order; I get it. Sex is one of those things that many of us are doing but pretend we don't do. This is why the thought of open discussions about sex gives us pause.

On the flip side, talking about the seemingly taboo is also HOT!

Banter of the salacious variety will add a certain je ne sais quoi to your life. Weaving a sexual thread into conversations, when appropriate, of course, will help you uncover your erotic potential.

Chat about sex with lovers and friends. Talk about it with strangers and familiars. You don't have to spill all the tea or share intimate details of your sexcapades. Just allow space for discussions about sex to become normal because life is sexually transmitted.

Normalizing conversations about sex creates safe spaces for sexual expression. While also reducing sexual frustration, which could potentially decrease sexual violence.

Being in dialogue with others is how we learn, grow, and evolve. Talking about sex is how we eradicate and disempower sexual shame. The more you do it, the better you will feel, all the while improving your sex life and up-leveling your pleasure potential.

3. PRACTICE RADICAL HONESTY

Pleasure requires truth-telling. #ForFacts

This is true in and out of the bedroom, whether you're having sex with yourself or another(s). To feel good, you have to keep it real. Because untruths inhibit pleasure. It's like holding your breath right before you cum.

Honesty is the fertilizer that helps trust grow. And truth be told, pun intended, pleasure is only accessible when you feel safe.

People who engage in honest communication have more robust connections. I should add that honest communication does not mean agreeing all time.

The ability to fully express yourself in the company of another or being transparent about yourself—with yourself—is a game-changer. When you open your heart, use your words, and live your truth, it permits others to do the same.

4. USE MASTURBATION LIKE MEDICINE

Getting familiar with your own body is not only revolutionary, but it's also extremely vulnerable. Shame around sex and sexuality is a trans-generational wound that has been hitchhiking on the double-helix for a very long time.

But I'm here to tell you that sexual healing is real. Sex in and of itself is transformative on a cellular level. Who you are at the start of a sexual experience is not who you are when it's done (good or bad).

Sexual healing isn't exclusive to partnered encounters. Solo-sex is therapeutic and nourishing too. After all, it's sex with someone you love, or at least it should be.

Masturbation is medicinal—it's a beeline to pleasure. Solo sex will shift your relationships. Make you more compassionate and empathetic. Becoming intimate with your body can deepen your connection with others. You may begin to have more engaging conversations. Your attention span could increase, leaving you feeling more in tune with your environment, with greater awareness of things you rarely noticed before.

You may experience an increase in energy, so you won't tire as quickly. Quality sleep and enhanced taste and smell are also potential side-effects. Best of all, your self-awareness will increase, which means deeper love and greater intimacy with others. It can get that good.

5. PRIORITIZE YOUR NEEDS

Feeling good makes life better. But to feel good, you have to know what you need and then make those things a priority. For sexual pleasure to be a blip on the radar, you need to know what conditions are required to make sex good for you.

Before musicians go on tour, they provide the venue with a tour rider. Which is "a document that includes a set of rules that a performer sets as criteria for a performance. This includes all requests or demands either for the artist's comfort or the technical details needed to perform."

I invite you to think about your needs as a tour rider.

What are your conditions for good sex?

Things to consider:

SELF

Self-esteem is the one universal requirement for a positive sexual experience. It doesn't matter who you are or where you come from; how you perceive yourself plays a huge role in whether sex is good or not.

You may never feel sexually proficient. But some things help you feel more comfortable with yourself, which makes sex better for you and your partner(s). Get clear about what those things are.

EMOTIONAL STATE

Think about the things that feel a bit overwhelming to you before or during sex. What would make you feel more settled?

I have found that meditation and intention setting help to ease apprehension for me. So I take the time to be still, if only for a few seconds, before every sexual encounter. And if time permits, I invoke an intention in advance.

Get curious, find out what works for you, and make it a part of your sexual preparation ritual.

ENVIRONMENT

The environmental conditions for sex will not always be perfect. And sometimes imperfect conditions make for a steamy good time. But more often than not, you will have at least a smidgen of control over where it all goes down. And when you do, make it optimal.

When it comes to sex, physical comforts are not a luxury; they are a requirement. Not always, but most of the time.

Ensure that your surroundings are free of any distractions that will take you out of your body and into your head. If cell-phone pings give you the jitters, turn the ringer off. You might have a hard time enjoying sex when the kids are at home. And if that's the case, you either need to have a workaround or a sitter.

Optimize your environment as much as reasonably possible so that you can focus on pleasure.

PARTNER

What makes you feel connected to your partner(s)? Regardless of the relationship's type or duration, having an emotional connection makes for better sex, period. You don't have to be in love or in a relationship to feel an emotional spark. Or maybe you do.

Do you trust this person? Do you feel safe in their company? Are you sexually excited at the thought of being together?

Do you feel seen? Are they a good listener? Have they made their boundaries clear? Do they respect and honor your boundaries?

Do you need a partner who is comfortable initiating sex? Do you prefer your partner to talk while sex is in process? Or do you prefer silence?

Remember, your partner's conditions are as important as yours. Being with someone that you can express yourself with improves the quality of the sexual experience. The ability to have open dialogue and negotiation makes good sex accessible to both of you.

...

We are living in unprecedented times. We have access to everything, and everything has access to us. And while sex has been commodified and commercialized, pleasure is still an act of rebellion.

You deserve to feel good. It is not something you need to earn. Your worth is not a factor because you are worthy, period. The only question that matters is whether you want to or not. There is no wrong answer. It is entirely up to you. You are free to choose.

Stacey Herrera is an Intimacy & REALationship coach, writer, and creator of The Sensuality Project, a lifestyle movement for 40+ singles and couples who want to improve their sex lives and have mature intimate relationships.

In Stacey's world, relationship-ing is about more than finding a right-fit partner and living happily ever after. Relationships inform the way we do business and how we treat our neighbors. It's about family — born and chosen. Because how you relate to the people around you can mean the difference between survival and fulfillment.

She believes that relationships are essential to our species' survival - like food, air, and water. Which is why her mission is to help people get really good at relating to one another. It's not just about creating happiness in our personal lives - it's about creating peace and unity for the entire human race.

Stacey resides in a charming town on the coast of California. She spends her free time getting lost in books, baking cookies and creating memories with her lovers, family, and friends.

CHAPTER 25

WRITING TO LIVE AGAIN

DISCOVERING HEALING POWER IN THE PEN

DINAHSTA *"MISS KIANE"* THOMAS, MSW, LGSW

MY STORY

Held firmly by the darkness around me, I sat helpless, quivering on the floor of what used to be *our* bedroom closet. "Our" refers to my mother and me. We shared a room in my grandmother's three-bedroom rancher. The previous year, my grandmother moved us from Omaha, Nebraska, to Salisbury, Maryland, to live with her. It was her way of keeping an eye on her daughter, especially after the last episode. My mother's mental illness seemed to warrant supervision.

I adored my mother. Yes, she *was* oddly eccentric, wildly unpredictable, and blatantly defiant. She had schizophrenia (at least that's what the doctors said back then). But she was also brilliantly creative, magnetically charismatic, and crazy-intelligent. She affirmed me. She saw me. She was my blanket in an otherwise very cold world. So, one can imagine when she died suddenly how very devastated a 12-year-old me must have been.

The pain was so intense I wanted to rip my soul out of my legs. For some odd reason, I believed that my soul resided in my legs. My mother asked me once, "Where do you think your soul is?" "Uhm…in my legs!" I retorted. She didn't object. She just nodded her head subtly. On this day, my legs were hollow, and every beat of my heart drove needles through my skin from the inside out. I *wanted* the pain to stop. I ***needed*** the pain to stop.

I wanted to die.

Quietly weeping in the darkness of that closet, I could feel my mother's scent raining on me from the clothes hanging above my head. I had decided to take my life. My weapon? A plastic bag. No pills, knives, or guns. Just a plastic bag. I was a novice to the suicide thing, but in that moment, the only objective was to stop the pain.

So, there I sat on the closet floor in the room next to my grandmother's with a plastic bag over my head, desperately trying to suffocate the pain. What I quickly learned was the body has a mechanism called self-preservation. Involuntarily my legs kicked, my torso jerked, and my lungs screamed for air. It turns out I was no match for my own body's will to live.

So, I decided to live, but I was still dying inside. I had no place to bleed in peace. There were no appointments made with counselors because "We don't talk about our business with strangers. We handle it at home." There was no one to talk to at home because "You just have to be strong and move on." There was no school counselor's office to hide in because the school counselor was a stranger and, "We don't tell our business to strangers."

I needed a new weapon, something stronger than a plastic bag; something that complimented my will to live. This time, I picked up a pen. I began to journal. I painted pictures of my pain like Picasso but with words. I found a safe space to bleed in peace. Phrases written in cursive lay on pages like a patient sprawled across the therapist's couch. I was the patient and my pen, the therapist.

Several years later, I still find healing in my pen. As a poet and safe space facilitator, I established a nonprofit called The InkWELL. The purpose of The InkWELL is to facilitate hope, awareness, and self-love through guided reflection and creative writing. Loss, trauma, and emotional distress are common experiences of the human race, and artistic interventions such as writing have proven effective.

THE TOOL

Are you experiencing loss? Feeling dead inside? Or maybe you just want a greater sense of self-awareness? I can help you start a reflective journey where your pen and pad are all you need! Before the journey can begin, however, you must first choose, decide, and commit. *Choose* the vehicle you will use to collect your thoughts. I still prefer a pen and pad. You may like electronic devices. *Decide* to be honest, transparent, and vulnerable. Reflection involves introspection; therefore, the only person you have to be accountable to is YOU. Lastly, *commit* to the process. Set a time, a frequency, and a place where you can focus on your journey.

Now your reflective journey can begin! There are three R's to remember in this journey; reflection, release, and replenish.

Reflection involves thinking about an incident or circumstance and sitting with the emotions that the incident or circumstance evokes. Write out the incident/circumstance. What has been the impact of this incident or circumstance in your life? This can be overwhelming, so it is important to break the topic of your reflections into emotionally manageable pieces.

Releasing speaks to letting go. Unleash your raw emotion onto the page. Write down how the incident or circumstance makes you feel. How are you feeling right now as you write (or type)? Be completely honest and transparent. After emptying out your feelings, you may feel physically depleted. Allow yourself space to rest and recover.

Replenish means to *fill up again.* After reflecting and releasing, write what "ah-ha" moments unfolded from your reflective writing time. What do you understand better about yourself? While it may be challenging to have an "ah-ha" moment every time you write, replenishing is where the healing takes place so just keep writing!

To learn more about the 3 R's, tune in to The InkWELL's video series on the Reflective Writing Journey at https://fb.watch/2JiLLE0r02/. Follow us on social media platforms Instagram (https://www.instagram.com/theinkwellproject/) and Facebook.

Dinahsta *"Miss Kiane"* Thomas, MSW, LGSW, is an author, performer, and safe space facilitator. She has extensive experience writing, directing, and performing in theatrical productions. Dinahsta has shared her poetry in several venues, including Café Muse, Sojourn with Words, Busboys and Poets and Storytellers. She was honored as the Poetry Society's Who's Who in Poetry. Dinahsta is currently the Administrator for a Facebook Group called Poets, Writers and Creative Scribblers, where she creates a virtual safe space for creatives to imagine, write, and connect. In addition, she enjoys hosting open mic nights at DC's newest Busboys and Poets in Anacostia and on their virtual platforms since the Pandemic.

In 2019, Dinahsta established a nonprofit called The InkWELL to facilitate hope, awareness, and self-love through guided reflection and creative writing. The InkWELL intends to provide safe and cathartic spaces for people to express themselves.

As a Licensed Graduate Social Worker, Dinahsta seeks to meld her profession and her passion to help others access healing, empowerment, and growth through the power of poetry, reflective writing, and creative expression.

HIRING A GUIDE

TAKING YOUR HEALTH TO THE NEXT LEVEL

All the experts here agree that empowering you by giving you tools to treat yourself at home is one of the keys to healing. When you take responsibility for self-awareness, self-care, self-healing, and self-development, you are much more apt to feel good and stay feeling that way. We've experienced clients who take self-treatment to heart getting better faster, staying healthier in the long run, and really enjoying their lives to the fullest.

We also know many people need skilled assistance and guidance to feel better. The clients we come across are in all stages of physical, mental, and emotional disease or dysfunction. Some need a quick tool and home program, while others require intensive or prolonged care. We all agree that having a guide on the journey is paramount to peak performance, whatever stage you're in.

When you have a guide, coach, or healer in your corner, you'll reach your goals faster, but more importantly, you'll have someone invested in your progress and healing, and you won't be doing it alone. Remember, that guide has been where you are, and has healed the layers you're going through. He or she is able to hold a healing space for you to do that same work. Holding a healing space for you means they've practiced a conscious presence, an ability to ground and center themselves, and an ability to energetically enhance your healing process. That conscious presence is not something you find in all people. It's a practice that healers have worked for years to master. They've adopted a lifestyle that includes these skills and tools, so they can help others. They are special, amazing people.

This final note is to encourage you to seek out a guide if you feel like you're stuck, not making progress, feeling more hopeless than hopeful, or just can't consistently get your mindset to stay positive, open, or clear. We encourage you to explore different modalities and different guides, coaches, and practitioners. Find someone you vibe with and hire them to help you get to where you want to go.

Try asking: What else is possible for my healing today? Just asking yourself that question should help you feel hopeful. Sit with that question without straining to hear an answer. Allow yourself to meditate on the possibility.

Another great question to sit with, and/or journal about: What if there's something you haven't learned yet that could change everything?

We sit around and think we've read it all, done it all, and learned it all, and we stay resigned to our current mediocre physical, mental, emotional status because we think there are no alternatives or options left. I've been exploring healing and the vast array of healing modalities for an entire lifetime, and I'm here to tell you I won't have time to get to all the possibilities.

The point here is there are people out there who will help you heal. There's a guide out there waiting to teach you something you didn't even know existed and expose you to another level of hope you didn't realize you could feel. This book outlines dozens of those approaches. Some traditional. Some alternative. Some you may have never heard of. Some you may have heard of but never tried. It's time to explore!

It's our job as authentic healers, practitioners, and guides to facilitate a process of healing in you, connect you with your inner healer and power, and super-boost that power inside you. And we're good at it. Try us!

Please go back to the chapters that drew you in, piqued your interest, or had you feeling a little excited. Look up the amazing author there and read a little bit more about them on their website. You might even contact them to say thank you for their words, or set up a call with them to discuss what you learned. The authors I asked to be a part of this are cool like that; they want you to feel better, and they are open-hearted, skilled, and very aware and experienced healers. They thrive when you thrive. It's part of their mission, like it is mine, to help heal the world.

I hope you enjoyed this book. Even more than that, I hope you're getting into action with it, trying the exercises and tools, and getting some results! I'd love to hear how you're doing. Hop over to www.BraveHealer.com and send me a note!

Lastly, I have a personal favor to ask. If you enjoyed this book and have a couple minutes to leave a review on Amazon, I'd greatly appreciate it. Your review helps others see our book, and it spreads the good vibes. Thank you!

Signing off now with a final wish for your best health. May you find what you need to thrive, mind, body, and soul.

With warrior love,

Laura

A RAMPAGE OF GRATITUDE

Gratitude is the energy I wanted to purposefully end the book with, in hopes you'll read this last page and imagine all the people in your own life you're grateful for, maybe even some of these fantastic authors!

This is more than acknowledging people for their help with this book, it's conjuring up energy we can take with us as we move forward into our purpose and mission of helping the world heal. Appreciation is the energy of manifestation! It's a magical, foundational mindset that everything good is born from.

So, amazing reader, thank you for being here! For being open to learning. And for exploring this fascinating world of healing with me and all of the authors here. You are powerful, and have limitless potential to heal yourself! Step into your power, use the tools, ask more questions, and adopt a lifestyle of learning. That's how you'll continue to evolve and feel the most peace, happiness, and health in the future. I'm so grateful to be walking alongside you on this journey.

To my authors, the badassery you've laid down on these pages is spectacular! In the many conversations I had with you during the writing phase of your chapters you gave me your trust, and allowed me to inspire you, even though you may have been unsure. You believed me when I told you how important your authentic stories are and you told them, without apology, and with a stupendous courage and generosity. Thank you for that.

Thank you for saying yes to this project! And thank you for stepping up to teach what you know and gift our readers with your unique expertise, knowledge and skills. I'm so honored to be in your company.

To our book designer, Dino Marino, thank you for stepping up to make this book shine, inside and out! You take on our collaborative projects with ease and grace and I'm so grateful to have you on our team.

To our front-cover artist, Jo Jayson. Thank you so much for being a part of this project and giving this book its face for the world. Your gorgeous goddess art has the energy of healing I'd dreamed of when I envisioned these books. Find Jo at www.JoJayson.com

To all our friends, family, colleagues, acquaintances and book launch team members who supported us during the writing, publishing, launching and promoting of this project, thank you so much for your support, love, words of encouragement, and purchases. This village is badass!

JOIN THE AUTHOR TEAM

FOR THE NEXT
ULTIMATE GUIDE TO SELF-HEALING BOOK!

Brave Healer Productions is now accepting applications to be part of our next book!

You're a healer…

…and a business owner, and you're ready to share your message with the world in a bigger way!

Contributing a chapter to this powerful collaborative project is much more than just having your name on a book.

It's about being part of a community of healthcare entrepreneurs who are changing the world with their brave words and tools.

Each author shares their story, and teaches an effective self-healing tool in their chapter. Authors then have opportunities to do live training, podcast interviews, and business development activities as a part of the Brave Healer Productions family.

We can't wait to hear your story!

Submit your application today! https://lauradifranco.com/ultimate-guide-project/

"All I can say is, if you have a book inside you, a message you want to gift the world, or a healing business you want to grow, there is no one better than Laura Di Franco, and Brave Healer Productions. She and her team will guide you through all the stages, from concept to writing to getting your book into the hands of your readers. She genuinely wants to bring health and healing to the world we all live in. And she delivers big time."

Dr. Shelley Astrof, Author of The Knower Curriculum

"It's one thing to have a process that will help a book become successful. It's a whole other thing to create success from a place of holding sacred space and unconditional warrior love for every person she works with to step into their capacity for brilliance. My heart is grateful for the innumerable ways Laura has created for authors to connect with readers."

Sharon Carne, Director of Training and Development, Sound Wellness

"Laura Di Franco is a master at helping your work take flight and land with your target audience. She has a unique ability to help you draw out your good ideas, and her experience in the world of writing quickly moves ideas to action. Laura has no shortage of ideas for your success and will give you more than you could imagine possible. Trust her to land your words!"

Dr. Erika Putnam, DC, RYT 500

OTHER BOOKS

BY LAURA DI FRANCO

- The Ultimate Guide to Self-Healing Techniques, Volume 1
- The Ultimate Guide to Self-Healing Techniques, Volume 2
- The Ultimate Guide to Self-Healing Techniques, Volume 3
- Living, Healing and Tae Kwon Do, a Memoir to Inspire Your Inner Warrior
- Brave Healing, a Guide for Your Journey
- Your High Vibe Business, a Strategic Workbook for Badass Entrepreneurial Success
- Joy Stacking: The 3 Step Formula to Authentic Success
- Warrior Love, a Journal to Inspire Your Fiercely Alive Whole Self
- Warrior Joy, a Journal to Inspire Your Fiercely Alive Whole Self
- Warrior Soul, a Journal to Inspire Your Fiercely Alive Whole Self
- Warrior Dreams, a Journal to Inspire Your Fiercely Alive Whole Self
- Warrior Desire, Love Poems to Inspire Your Fiercely Alive Whole Self

ADDITIONAL BOOKS FROM BRAVE HEALER PRODUCTIONS

- The Wellness Universe Guide to Complete Self-Care: 25 Tools for Stress Relief, by Anna Pereira
- The Wellness Universe Guide to Complete Self-Care: 25 Tools for Happiness, by Anna Pereira
- Find Your Voice, Save Your Life, by Dianna Leeder
- Family Fuel: A Busy Mom's Guide to Healthy Living for the Family, by Jennifer Wren Tolo, RN, MA

Your words will change the world when you're brave enough to share them. Your fear of not-good-enough is boring. What if the thing you're still a little afraid to share is exactly what someone needs to hear to change, or even save their life? It's time to be brave.

~Laura Di Franco

Made in the USA
Middletown, DE
11 March 2021